Emily Ford's
Pillow Book

THE *Erotic* Print Society
EPS, 1 Maddox Street
LONDON W1S 2PZ

Tel (UK only): 0800 026 25 24
Fax: +44 (0)20 7437 3528
Email: *eros@eroticprints.org*
Web: *www.eroticprints.org*

ISBN 1-898998-50-7

Printed and bound in Spain by Bookprint, S.L., Barcelona

Emily Ford's
Pillow Book

THE *Erotic* Print Society

Would you allow your wife or your servant to read this book?

Mervyn Griffith-Jones

(for the Crown in the *Lady Chatterley's Lover* trial, 1960)

Foreword

Dear Reader,

I have something of an embarrassing admission to make: until just the other day I was a virgin.

Even though my affair with the Erotic Print Society publishing house has lasted seven years or more (I think that constitutes one of the Ages of Man, and is more enduring than a lot of marriages I know), until now I remained utterly virginal when it came to putting my name on a book. Surrounded by writers, artists, photographers and other individuals generally immersed in the world of the erotic, who think nothing of dashing off a paperback here or an article there, it was hard to rub shoulders (and occasionally different parts of our anatomies) with those who were so blasé about their book launch parties and signing sessions and not feel just a twinge of jealousy now and then. Then one of them suggested – rather kindly, I thought – that I should join their club.

So here it is – proof, like the bloodied sheet proudly held aloft – my authorship in letters bold and high. All right, all right, I haven't actually written the wretched thing. My *Pillow Book* is a selection of my favourite erotic short stories, articles, illustrations and photographs by authors, artists and photographers for whom I have a high regard. We've even got a complete pornographic Victorian novella, fully illustrated by the incomparable Sylvie Jones, an erotic Æsop's fable deliciously delineated by Tim Major, crosswords, little pictorial essays of both art or photography... the list isn't exactly endless, but I would like to think that there's enough here to keep you busy for a rainy afternoon. I'm sorry that I have had to leave out a few, for the sake of a homogenous whole, but you can't very well bake a cake using all the ingredients in the kitchen cupboard. Everyone here has been enormously kind in helping me make my selection, but by and large this is an eclectic grouping of bits and pieces that reflects my own rather varied and quirky tastes.

Whether procreative or recreational, sex fascinates me as one of the most powerful yet least liberated of human activities. There are often cogent arguments for why various cultures 'sweep it all under the carpet' and, by and large, I respect them. I'm not an anthropologist but there seems to be a certain rhythm to the ebb and flow of sexual awareness and enjoyment in many different societies, and of how sex (or fear of it) is sometimes used as a political or religious device to control society.

Then there's sex and the individual. I'm no psychoanalyst, either, but it doesn't take a Freud or a Jung to know that one of the chief inspirations in life is the all-consuming need to find and fuck the perfect mate as often as is humanly possible until our attention is distracted by an even more perfect specimen of the opposite (or same) sex. It leads to all sorts of entertaining situations, both emotional and physical, and keeps florists and restaurateurs, gossip columnists and paparazzi, agony aunts and uncles, jewellers and chocolatiers, lawyers and counsellors, matchmakers and sex workers (as we must now term our sisters of the night) and even me, extremely busy.

Though neither sex is particularly keen to admit it, this happy pursuit sometimes comes adrift. But then for inspiration we can always turn to erotic art and literature to enhance our sexual fantasies and exercise what is, despite recent discoveries about the full and impressive extent of the clitoris, commonly thought to be the largest sexual organ – the brain.

This book isn't solely designed for individuals who prefer to pursue the 'solitary vice' (not that I'm being censorious here: 'Don't knock it, it's sex with someone you love' Woody Allen once said of masturbation). I hope that as many of you as possible will enjoy this book, singly, *à deux* or in groups, to share, to hand around the table after dinner or to read aloud beside the pool, or – if you happen to be in California – in the hot tub. And I hope it will bring you as much enjoyment as it did me putting it together.

Best wishes and erotic dreams,

Emily

Emily Ford

A man with an erection is in no need of advice.

Samuel Pepys

Come
with
Me

Come with me Stephen Bayley

Gregory the Great demanded that a seducer of a virgin, whatever *that* is, must marry her or, failing the discharge of this honourable obligation, suffer severe corporal punishment before being banged up in a monastery to perform enduring and solitary penance. St Thomas Aquinas said that lust, even in the slightest degree, was a mortal sin. The liberals among the doctors of the church allowed that a premarital touch of the hand was acceptable provided only that absolutely no sexual feelings were stimulated. So, nuzzling the ear, inhaling shampoo, quickening breath, muttering poetry, solidifying and liquefying groins, a firm breast in one hand, knicker elastic in the other, a shuffling of position, an arching back, a click, a snap, a bustle, a zip, a 'don't' and then a 'do', an 'ooh' and an 'ah'. This is modern life.

Somewhere between the Middle Ages and now we developed sophisticated stratagems of seduction. Ovid's *Ars Amatoria* was an important Roman predecessor of the how-to book, a welcome rediscovery of the Renaissance. The art of courtly love – or how to get your leg over an obstinate strumpet with the help of troubadours – was defined in a twelfth-century treatise by Andreas Capellanus. Castiglione, Machiavelli, Gracian and later Choderlos de la Clos, not to mention Casanova, all contributed to the body of expertise in getting a reluctant woman to make the journey from no to yes. All these great philosophers of manners have their champions, although some say Terry Southerri's *Flash and Filigree* (1958) is the masterpiece of the genre. Here the man calms with his voice while arousing with his hands, although the inept get it the wrong way around. 'No. Not there, you idiot,' for some reason comes echoing back into the cavernous hall of memory.

So. Seduction. How do you do it? I think tact is important. In normal circumstances I don't find the gallant invitation 'Do you want to fuck me, big boy?' much of an inducement, although it is quite unusual, thus achieving the interesting condition of being both rare and worthless. John Gay's *The Beggar's Opera* says:

> 'Tis woman that seduces all mankind
> By her we first were taught the wheedling arts.

I'm not sure wheedling does much for me either. Equally, I think most men don't like women's initiative in this area. I used to know a successful couple in property development who visited building sites in a burgundy Rolls-Royce Camargue with cream upholstery. The wife was a handsome woman with lustrous hair down to her waist and an astonishing dress-sense which included fishnet tights, leather hotpants, stiletto patent boots, a leopard-skin handbag and translucent black shirt with a great deal going on underneath. I asked her why and she said it was a navvy-survival technique. Brute men on sites were so taken aback they were muted.

Again, a 1980s entrepreneur claimed that the scariest moment he had had was when, at tea in Downing Street, the Prime Minister put her hand on his leg, looked him in the eye, and said, 'You know something? It is very lonely for a woman here.'

I have my own contender. Years ago at a conference I sat next to exactly the sort of woman I find stirringly attractive. French. Simple skirt, good shoes, plain cashmere V-neck. Nice hair, the accent, a twinkle in the eye, bookish, but dangerous with an untipped Gitane. We progressed to dinner and I was loving it all until, back in the car she said, 'And now I want you to drive me to the country, remove my *petites culottes* and have me in a field.'

This was Bloomsbury at midnight so you can see the problem. Or take Norman Lewis, as another French woman tried to at a dreadful Embassy dinner. Next to him at table she lifted her skirt and said '*Voulez-vous voir ma petite craque?*' This doesn't work. Instead, a flick of the hair, an indeterminate sigh, and a distracted look are what does it for me. Although if by any chance Natalie is reading this, I hope you agree I made up for it by the time we got to Amersham.

Like Natalie, my own stratagems are now history; now that the relative certainties of marriage have replaced the vagaries of independent life. But, thinking back, it was John Gay who, again, understood seducers' techniques

What cannot a neat knave with a smooth tale
Make a woman believe?

When I was a neat knave I always found Andrew Marvel's 'To his Coy Mistress' worked wonders. It was written as a seducer's manifesto, but you had to be certain the listener was sensitive to nuance. More direct approaches can work too. We have all known someone who has said the practice of asking every woman he met whether she would like to 'tear her pleasure with rough strife through the iron grates of life' right now yields surprisingly high statistical positives. I have never, alas, tried this, although I recall there was one striking success when, despairing of subtleties, I simply had the nerve to say, 'I've come here ("here" was West Hampstead so it was no laughing matter) tonight because I think you're the most attractive woman I have ever met.' Minutes later, the fragrances of an unfamiliar bedroom. That was a lie and it felt like it the next morning.

The seducer, especially the male seducer, is always on dubious moral ground because the concept implies an element of coercion. The erotic element in seduction is not just the hoped-for climax at the top of the sexual mountain, but the element of power relations involved in all the processes required on the lower slopes. Rather as Stirling once said of motor racing that, 'if it wasn't dangerous, anyone could do it', with seduction, it's the same. While the joyful spasm of the groin might be a welcome brute pleasure, if every one was just there to be had on demand, then an orgasm would not be so very much different to a sneeze (which it happens to resemble neurologically). If seduction was not so difficult, it would not be so engrossing.

And it can still be dangerous. One of my favourite novellas is Nathanial West's *Miss Lonelyhearts* (1933). Here the narrator, a male agony columnist, seduces a frustrated reader out of charity and, as I recall, gets shot for his kindness. As ever it's best (not?) to think about it.

This article first appeared in The Erotic Review

License my roving hands, and let them go
Before, behind, between, above, below.
O my America, my new-found land,
My kingdom, safeliest when with one man manned,
My mine of precious stones, my empery,
How blessed am I in thus discovering thee!
To enter in these bonds, is to be free;
Then where my hand is set, my seal shall be.

John Donne

Fantasy & Fear

Fantasy & Fear

Justine Dubois

They share an early supper. She dresses demurely, in black. He arrives straight from work, pinstriped. The restaurant is just a few streets away; a boisterous, fashionable corridor running between the pavement and its own kitchen. On either side, men bowed down by the self-importance of work succeed in looking both bored and animated. Next to them sit women, disdainfully pretty in floral chic. The waiter brings them a menu.

She is translucent-skinned and youthful, her auburn hair a confection of unruly curls. Opposite her, the Prussian blue of his shirt matches his eyes. He is straight-backed and aquiline, with single plumes of grey at his forehead. He is charmingly unaware of his own good looks.

The waiter brings them pasta, steeped in squid ink. Around them, the restaurant is a hubbub of animation, but their concentration on each other is far greater. They are like fierce lovers in a Watteau landscape. Everyone else is at play; only they are serious. Their love makes no attempt to exclude, and yet always succeeds effortlessly in so doing. Slowly, the room begins to revolve around their passion. Covert glances, part-envy, part-amazement stalk them. Yet, they only see each other. They talk keenly, their faces alight with delicious smiles. They share a dish of strawberries decorated with mint, white-veiled in sugar. He pays the bill and then orders himself an extra coffee. 'Are you having something more to drink?' he asks.

'No, nothing, thank you. I am leaving.' She stands up.

'Won't they think you are deserting me?'

'I expect you can bear the ignominy of it,' she teases. A moment of panic.

'But I assumed...' She smiles and makes to walk out. 'There is something I need to do, a surprise. Join me in ten minutes if you like.'

At home, she climbs the stairs. She throws her keys onto the bed, then removes her top layer of clothing; the anonymous polo-neck, the dark skirt. She exchanges her mid-height heels for something more precipitous. She only retains her emerald and gold earrings, which dazzle in her reddish hair.

Beneath the banality of her outer garments, she is no longer anonymous. At her waist is a suspender belt of black, beribboned satin, its suspenders dragged low over the long, smooth-stockinged curve of her thighs. Her figure is round, shapely. The bra she wears is like a hieroglyph, a signal of support, but curiously ineffectual. Her breasts tumble from its constraining architecture like ripe fruit. A red rosebud sits coyly at the centre of its divisive under-bridge. As if to make up for its faulty design, its bra straps are broad and fat with expensive black lace, the same quipure lace that fails to veil her nipples. She checks her watch; only a few minutes to go. She twists her hair into a chignon and secures it with a black velvet ribbon-bow, attached to a silver clip. He always likes to see the swan length of her slender neck.

She is rushing now. She searches, last minute, in a drawer, her supple body jackknifing gracefully on her vertiginous heels. She finds what she is looking for, a mask, a plain sleeper's mask; no feathers, no allusive cat features to enhance its design, simply a pragmatic mask, with which to cut out light and sight. As she stands up, she remembers her panties, black butterflies flocked onto filmy chiffon. She steps from them and they curl on the carpet, like a hair-net. The cat pounces on them, ready to play. The ten minutes are up. She dashes to the front door and opens it, leaving it slightly ajar. She then returns to the subdued lighting of the sitting-room and, with one last-minute glance at herself in the mirror, fastens the mask over her eyes. She then positions herself on the sofa, arms stretched outwards along its high back, her legs spread invitingly wide.

She waits. The minutes pass intensely. She experiences a moment of sharp *frisson*. The front door is open. Anyone can enter. She feels blind, vulnerable, exposed. Seconds of darkness feel like an eternity of waiting. Fantasy and fear invade her every sense. Her hearing grows unusually acute. She finds herself interpreting every stray noise. No one arrives. She hears the creak of a distant floorboard, followed by the shrill of a siren from the street. Again silence. Her fear mounts tantalisingly. She feels a sudden draught of cold air. No sound. She is stranded in darkness. There are slight echoes of movement. By now, she is keyed-up, her feelings polarised, both confident and afraid. She struggles to maintain her composure. From beneath her mask slip involuntary smiles. His tongue, as it is placed full against her, feels like a sable brush, plump with pigment. It is the most delicious sensation. No one speaks. He is familiar, and yet not completely so. The doubt is exciting. All her senses are alert to every nuance of his touch.

He uses his mouth like an instrument. His hands have not yet touched her, simply the clever explorations of his fat tongue. The cage of her hips rises to greet him in silence. His tongue washes over her and then seeks out her mouth. The muzzle of his face is wet against hers. She can taste herself in the *longueur* of his kisses.

Now, at last, his hands are upon her. He touches her nipples, as they tumble from their confining lace, and murmurs his approval. He drags her low in the lap of the sofa, her buttocks arched forward. She feels his penis brush against the warmth of her thighs as he enters her. And now, almost familiar, the sense of him within her. But still a hint of surprise. His energies blend with hers, bounce within her.

He turns her round, cupping her breasts to enter her from behind. He is about to lose control. He withdraws. Blindfolded, silent still, he leads her upstairs, feet faltering, carefully negotiating her way. She is disorientated. Her feet stumble on the stairs. She stands still, listening, whilst he opens various doors. She is perplexed. He leads her forward. He stretches her out on the bed, lengthening his frame over hers. He feels capable, strong. He kisses her ardently. Her perfume has become an amalgam of scents. She raises the cat's cradle of her hips in welcome; sweet familiarity. Then, something new, he bites her neck. Together they race incoherently. He leans back, kneeling between her legs to kiss her. She is close, so very close. Sensations of sweetness envelop her. Her body speeds to voracious silence. She calls out. He clasps her briefly, subsiding in his arms.

And then, still wrapped in darkness, she mounts him, riding him as he had previously ridden her. They fit together well. She can feel the draw of his flesh on hers. She clasps to his midriff like a buckle. They lose momentum, briefly. To alter the rhythm, she sits up tall, breasts bouncing. Beneath her mask, she smiles gladly and stretches her hand behind her to caress him lightly. It is the extra touch-paper of ignition. The sound of footsteps on the stairs. They had forgotten to close the front door. His body races in a fit of pleasure and submission. Her features are suffused with happy warmth. She makes to discard her mask triumphantly.

Her husband's voice calls, 'Sorry to have kept you, darling... An old friend of mine arrived at the restaurant just as I was leaving. It would have been rude not to talk...' She turns in desperation towards the door. Her happiness becomes distress.

Behind her stands her husband, surveying the baroque carnage of her lovemaking. As he does so, the blond, handsome stranger rises from their bed.

This short story first appeared in The Erotic Review

She feels his penis brush against the warmth of her thighs as he enters her. And now, almost familiar, the sense of him within her. But still a hint of surprise.

Fantasy and Fear

The only unnatural sex act is that which you cannot perform.

Alfred Kinsey

SEX AND CARS

Anonymous.

Anonymous

Wilkins

Wilkins.

Wilkins

Erotic is when you do something sensitive
and imaginative with a feather. Kinky is
when you use the whole chicken.

John Collee

Flogging a

Dead Frog

Flogging a Dead Frog
Richard Smithson

Sadly, the Marquis de Sade died in 1814, twenty-two years before Leopold von Sacher-Masoch was born. History was therefore deprived of a beautiful symbiotic relationship[1], although the fact that the former would have been 100 years old on the latter's fourth birthday makes it seem unlikely that the Marquis would have been able to administer the kicking that the Count so richly deserved.

Without wanting to sound too much like the hairy-chested hetero I so plainly am, I have never really warmed to Sacher-Masoch. Of course, we have all at some time wanted to be whipped like a dog at the feet of a woman dressed in furs — I know I have — but he does go *on* about it so. And it really doesn't seem to be any fun. In *Venus in Furs*, he describes a scene in which, when he was a child, his aunt entered the room in her fur-lined jacket with the cook, kitchen-maid and cat[2]. Naturally, it all ends in tears (bound hand and foot... whipped by his evil aunt... blood... tears... etc) but the effect is a little spoiled by the rather plonking morals that he will insist on drawing the whole time[3]: 'Now you understand the suprasensual fool! Under the lash of a beautiful woman my senses first realised the meaning of woman!' Yes, yes, yes, get on with it.

Not only that, but the whining little toad doesn't come once in all the interminable pages of his book — which, let me remind Mr So-Called Erotic Writer, is *supposed* to be all about sex[4]. It may be that he had the good sense to realise that if he came all over his wife's fur coat she would beat him to a pulp for real, and not stop when he gave the password either. (Of course, if you are the President of the USA you can come over any bloody clothing you like, and the silly girl will keep the stained garment as a souvenir. Can you imagine Sacher-Masoch sticking a cigar up Wanda?) Or perhaps I am missing the point. Perhaps it isn't about sex at all, any more than post-football communal baths are — just a healthy opportunity to get a lot of testosterone off your chest, and incidentally sit in a hot bath with your foot on your best friend's willy.

The Marquis de Sade is much easier to understand: harassed by his mother-in-law and imprisoned in the Bastille for most of his adult life[5], it is not surprising that his imagination ran riot. What is unforgivably sadistic was his fondness for amateur theatricals, which he indulged in to captive audiences at Charenton asylum[6]. De Sade (known to the French as 'the Divine Marquis', which may only be in comparison with Edith Cresson) was simply a dirty old man writ large.

If he hadn't been French, I dare say he would have been forgotten by now, but it is no use pointing out to our Gallic cousins that *Justine* and *120 Days of Sodom* are the most unmentionable tripe; they dearly love a philosopher, and the fact that they can't understand a word he is saying doesn't prevent them from stopping Jacques Derrida in the street and offering to have his babies. No, no, the Divine Marquis was just off his rocker

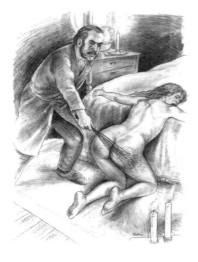

– as who wouldn't be after tossing himself off six times a day for three years.

What would the Marquis have done if he had met the Count? Sacher-Masoch was fastidiously clean, and a natty dresser, and de Sade's coprophilia would have been very upsetting, especially in the days before dry-cleaning. On the other hand, even in his obese old age the Marquis retained a certain dignity, grace and elegance, whereas you just know that Leopold would have had absolutely no small-talk, and would get all clammy and agitated when a strapping *hausfrau* hove into view, especially if she was wearing a day-glo, fun-fur crop-top and bondage trousers.

What they would have had in common if they ever had met can only be a matter of speculation. (You don't say.) I like to think that the Count's father would have tried to do the best for his son, and asked the ageing Marquis to stand as godfather if he ever got out of prison. Clearly, as the Marquis would have been 117 years old when von Sacher-Masoch came of age, physical intimacy (other than a palsied handshake) would have been out of the question; but it would be nice to think that the old man would have reflected that since he could no longer bugger his godson, the very least that he could do would be to send him a Valentine card with a picture of a young woman in a fur coat whipping a pallid young man with a drooping moustache[7,8]. In exchange, the Count could offer his speckled and quavering buttocks for inspection, safe in the knowledge that no harm could come to them in that company.

The Emperor Heliogabalus offered a fortune to anyone who could invent a new vice[9], but the reward went unclaimed in his lifetime. How come France came up with sadism, and Germany with masochism? Why isn't there a seminal Estonian novel about a young man who sniffed women's bicycle seats[10], leading to a whole sub-culture of bicycle-seat sniffing, and an international Internet network of clandestine inhalers? What about an Englishman force-feeding his excrement to middle-aged women?[11] There must be a whole world of unusual practices waiting to twang the wires of a generation so jaded that the follollopy Charlie Dimmock is the last word in titillation.

Now that sadism has been replaced by fetishism, and masochism by Andrew Lloyd Webber, we need a new perversion for the new millennium. Something to get the juices flowing. Or not, as the case may be; I don't want to cramp your style. It shows the deplorable spinelessness of Cool Britannia that nowhere in the Millennium Dome was there the slightest hint of how we might be getting our jollies in the 21st century. De Sade was an innovator, but he couldn't have expected his particular practices to be the last word. He must be turning in his grave.

NOTES

1 Similar, for example, to the pairing of William Tell with Saint Sebastian, or Tracey Emin with Blind Pew.

2 The cat plays no further part in the story.

3 So German.

4 His wife Wanda wrote a book of memoirs in which she said what a drag it was to have to dress up in a fur coat and beat the crap out of her recalcitrant spouse. It sounds a pretty cushy life to me. (Though curiously enough she doesn't seem to have come at all in the course of her marriage, either.) She should think herself lucky she wasn't married to the Marquis de Sade. Or Gary Bushell.

5 He estimated that in the first three years of imprisonment he masturbated 6,600 times ie six times a day: once before breakfast, once at elevenses, once at lunch (usually missing the repeat of the Archers), once in mid-afternoon, once just before dinner (getting there just before the Archers), and once with his bedtime cocoa. With the benefit of television he could have timed himself by the frequent appearances of Carol Vorderman.

6 The Charenton Asylum Players' 1790 production of *The Mikado*, with Madame Defarge, Charlotte Corday and Robespierre as the Three Little Maids from School, had to be seen to be believed. 'Strong ensemble playing was sadly let down by an interpolated scene in which Nanki-Poo tore off Yum-Yum's head and defecated down the hole in her neck.' *Le Figaro*.

7 On Valentine's day in Wales it is traditional to present your love with a wooden spoon. Says it all really. Just another thing that Michael Douglas will have to get used to.

8 This sentence gives the unfortunate impression that she is using the moustache to whip him. Hang on, though, that's an idea...

9 'At Rome he did nothing but send out agents to search for those who had particularly large organs and bring them to the palace in order that he might enjoy their vigour.'

10 For whom the technical word is a 'snoob', after Arvo Snoeb, its author.

11 Ask Jeffrey Archer's publisher.

This article first appeared in The Erotic Review

Home is heaven and orgies are vile
But you need an orgy once in a while.

Ogden Nash

Wet Wet Wet

Wet wet wet Christine Pountney

I have recently taken up swimming again at my local leisure centre. I'm a good swimmer and over the last few weeks, have increased in strength and speed. The other day I actually hit a young man in the face while passing him in the opposite direction. I didn't do it intentionally of course, and managed to gurgle a bubbly 'Sorry' as I continued on my way, but eventually he moved into a slower lane. In retrospect, this may have done something in the way of singling me out to people who, unbeknownst to me, had their eye on me. People who belong to a secret society of nocturnal swimmers that I want to tell you about.

What I am about to describe only happened to me once. I've never seen them since, nor will I ever, in all likelihood, see them again. That is my only regret.

But for now, all I will say is that I had begun to notice my own growing complicity in a kind of aquatic pecking order. It had also begun to dawn on me that swimming in a public pool is a lot like flirting in a public house. There is a strict but unspoken protocol, a natural migration of people into smaller, more compatible groups, ways of getting closer to the object of your curiosity and arousal, and ways of putting distance in between, or even eliminating the competition.

Hypnotised by the repetition and exertion of my own muscular movements, I would often become aware of the other bodies only as electrical currents, like strip lights passing in a tunnel. Occasionally, a leg would brush my own or a hand claw at my waist, sometimes noticeably enough to arouse my curiosity concerning the author of these gestures. This is when the flirting would begin. Packaged as innocuously as a beneficial physical activity, people often overlook the extent to which swimming provides the perfect opportunity for voyeurism. It is almost impossible, when following close on the heels of another swimmer, not to perform an intimate inspection of their body. How could a man not enjoy watching the hourglass shape of a woman's gusset bisecting her body as, ass high up in the water, her long legs keep flying open like springs? And how could a woman, feeling a man approaching her from behind, not resist parting her legs even wider while doing the breast stroke, only to feel a deliciously achy sensation deep within her anus every time she reaches out with her toes.

There was a day not long ago when I was sure I was being followed. When I sped up, the man behind me did too, effortlessly, and yet he never passed me either. I could almost feel the heat of his body when, crowded together at the end of the lane, I would slow down to somersault. Pushing off the wall with my feet, I would practically have to swim underneath him as I angled over to the other side. I could feel his eyes caressing my skin and, after a while, I actually began to feel sexually excited by his proximity, by the bullying, intrusive way he had of following so close behind.

It was almost like fucking. Lap after exhausting lap, every time I pulled my arms in, scooping water into my chest then snapping straight as an arrow and surging forward, I could imagine him penetrating me.

And all the while, right there in front of me, as if I was just another link in a long chain of bodies, swam the vision of a plump but sturdy woman, breasts pushed out to the sides, thighs rippling like cream, the dark line of her burgundy bathing suit not more than two inches wide across her vulva.

She was a strong swimmer and as I followed her, I too felt as if I was chasing her, trying to get close enough to flick a finger under her gusset, pull it aside and slip my tongue into her wet sex.

When I got out of the pool I was flushed and delirious. I walked slowly to the changing room, regal as a drunk and long-forgotten beauty queen, the lactic acid already stiffening my muscles from the effort I'd made, my whole body pulsing and tingling with adrenalin.

I got under the shower head and closed my eyes. When I opened them, the woman I'd been swimming behind was standing beside me with her bathing suit pulled down around her waist, soaping her breasts.

'Hi,' she nodded.

'Hi,' I said back, watching her lean against the shower button. 'You know, if you screw the knob to the right, the shower stays on and you don't have to keep pressing it.'

'Thanks,' she said and smiled. 'My name's Kate, by the way.'

'I'm Shalla,' I said and held out my hand.

The next time I saw her she was standing just outside the leisure centre. I had been for a swim, showered and was heading home. She was standing on the kerb outside the building with a man around the same age. She was wearing a thick army-green parka with a fur-lined hood and a bright green backpack that matched her eyes. The man she was with was tall and handsome and had a strong jaw like an all-American male model. He was wearing a jean jacket and a pair of jeans and carrying a brown bag slung across his chest.

'Shalla,' she said. 'I want you to meet Dean.'

'Hi Dean,' I said, shaking his warm hand. He didn't seem to want to let go of it.

'We were waiting for you. We wanted to give you this,' she said. 'We hope you can come.' Then she leaned forward and kissed me on the cheek. Dean did the same and then they were off.

I looked down at the envelope she had given me. It was made of purple card, the texture of hand-made paper. I opened it and pulled out a gold square with black writing. Bordered by mermaids on either side, the following was written:

> *Let the secret society of underwater love-makers,*
> *drench you with pleasure on the next full moon.*
> *By personal invitation only*

I stared at the invitation in disbelief and yet, at the same time, my heart began to beat wildly.

Over the next few days, the moon waxed into a pale round face and then it was time. I dressed carefully and put my swimsuit in a bag, although I wasn't sure I was going to need it. Outside, the night was cold and starry; backyards and parking lots looked eerie and exposed in the moon's silver gleam.

When I got to the leisure centre, it looked completely deserted. For a moment I felt like I'd been duped and a wave of humiliation washed over me. Then the door opened slowly, and a man holding a candle beckoned me inside, his elongated shadow flickering on the ceiling.

'Come on in,' he said, closing the door behind me. 'I'm afraid I'm going to have to ask you to give me everything you're wearing before you go in.'

'What?' I asked.

'Don't worry. This isn't a trick,' he said and opened the door to what usually served as the reception office. The room was filled with neat little piles of clothing, all tagged and organised, sitting on top of bags and pairs of shoes. 'Everyone's equal beyond this point,' he said.

'But you're not undressed,' I said.

'That's because I'm the doorman.'

'Right,' I said. I took a deep breath, handed him my bag and began to undress. When I bent over to pull my underwear off the ends of my feet, he reached out and ran a hand over my ass. I stood up and he bent forward and kissed my breasts, sucking on each nipple before straightening up and pointing me towards a door.

'That way lies paradise,' he said and gave me a little push.

I gave him one final look, then walked across the hall and through a door. A row of candles were arranged on the floor creating a pathway I assumed I should follow. My body was now alight with an irresistible curiosity, which was magnetically pulling me forward. I could feel the doorman's saliva drying on my nipples, and the cool linoleum beneath my bare feet. I padded softly down the hall following the murmur of sighs coming from around the corner.

The trail of candles ended just in front of the men's locker room. The door was propped open and steam was curling around the door-jamb and spiralling slowly in the light. I ventured forward and in the shadows all around me I thought I could discern a few slow, undulating shapes, a man's arm and shoulder, bulging with muscles and glistening with sweat, a head of wet hair thrown back and slapped across a woman's pale back. There were a few more candles burning in the room, barely enough to see by, and I could hear the hissing of the showers. I groped my way towards them and, as I got closer, the steam became so dense it was like fog. I stood at the edge of the tiles, feeling the wisps of heat like tongues on my skin. Someone tapped me on the shoulder and I turned to see Dean's smiling face.

'Hi there,' he said.

'Hi Dean,' I said, grateful for the familiarity of his face. He took my hand and put it on his erection.

'Do you want to take a shower?' he whispered, nuzzling my neck.

He turned me around and held me under the hot water, then pivoted the nozzle so it was aimed at the wall and pushed me into the spray. He held me sideways against the wall with a forearm braced across my shoulders and prodded me with his cock, rubbing the tip forward along my cunt to my clitoris and back again. Before I could make sense of what was going on, he was bending me over and entering me from behind. He pushed me so far forward that I had to reach a hand out to steady myself and found myself touching a woman's back.

She was on her knees giving a man a blow-job, but when she felt my hands on her shoulders, she turned around, raised her chest to my face and put a breast in my mouth. Then she crawled underneath me, and while I leaned on her buttocks, she put her tongue next to Dean's penis and licked my clitoris. I reached around her ass and slipped my fingers into her cunt, while the man she'd been sucking straddled her, grabbed me and put his dick in my mouth.

For the next few minutes we were like a well-oiled machine, rising and falling, pulling and jerking and tensing and thrusting in unison. Just as I was about to come, Dean pulled out abruptly and said, 'Let's go for a swim. I don't want to come just yet. It's good to wait – and you. You're driving me crazy, baby.' Dazed and breathless, I followed him to the pool area where what seemed like a hundred naked bodies were writhing in and out of the water, silver and glistening in the moonlight which poured in like skimmed milk through a skylight in the ceiling. 'Who are all these people?' I whispered to Dean.

'You'd never guess,' he said and led me to the water's edge. As soon as I had slipped into the pool, a dozen pairs of hands were on my body, smothering my skin, probing every orifice, a finger in my mouth, another in my anus. Dean had disappeared and I was trapped in a bramble of anonymous limbs. I couldn't fight the collective strength of their avid caresses and decided to give myself over to the sensation. Suddenly, however, someone was pushing me underwater. I struggled to free myself but was held down. A man positioned himself underneath me and penetrated me. Hands were released and I came up gasping for breath. The man who was inside me was in front of me now, holding my legs around his waist, while another man, standing behind him, was penetrating him. This man was clutching my hips, sandwiching the man who was inside me. This man was looking over my shoulder at a man who had come up behind and gently penetrated my ass.

I have never been penetrated by two men at once and my whole pelvic area felt tight and on fire. I was held in place so tightly that I couldn't move and yet all around me these strong male bodies were slowly pumping and grinding. And then all of a sudden, as if on cue, we plunged underwater again. I was held down for what seemed like forever – 30, 40 seconds. I began to fight for breath and yet I couldn't deny the exquisite sensation of skin rubbing against skin, of a cock in my cunt and one in my ass, sliding in and out.

Just when I was resigned to an ecstatic death by drowning, we resurfaced and the moment I sucked air into my lungs, my whole lower body began to contract with the most powerful orgasm I have ever had. Urged on by my cries, the men continued to fuck me, harder at first and then slowing considerately as my breathing began to slow down too. Then they swam off in search of other prey and I was left alone, holding the edge of the pool, floating on my back. Someone approached me and kissed me lightly on the shoulder. 'Shalla, it's me, Kate.'

'Oh, god, Kate, am I ever happy to see you.' She put her mouth on mine and dragged me underwater... To this day, I have never seen her again. Or Dean, for that matter, who was so kind to me. He found me later that night, asleep on a bench under a towel. 'You must be tired,' he said. 'Can we take you home?' I nodded and he escorted me to the door. He kissed me goodnight and left me with the doorman, who helped me get dressed again. When he opened the door, daylight was breaking and there was a car waiting. The doorman put me in the back seat and told the driver to take me home. He even knew my address but I was too exhausted to question him.

On the way home, I had a fleeting wish that my driver would stop in a dark alley, and rape me in the back, but he too was a gentleman to the end, and even waited until I had closed my front door before driving away.

This short story first appeared in The Erotic Review

Pillow Book

Crossword 1

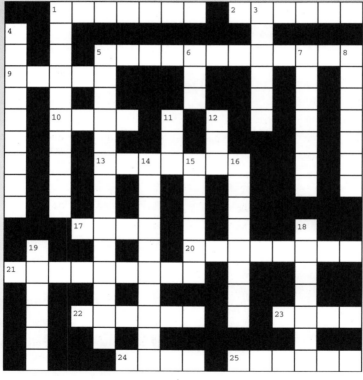

Solution on page 222

ACROSS

1 Not the real thing, more an artistic representation of the penis (7)

2 He of the Secret Life (6)

5 Peevish? No, I'm just a trannie! (12)

9 Artificial Penis (5)

10 Fun, but lonely, activity that rhymes with Midland Bank (4)

13 Well, kiss my arse... (7)

17 If you get these, you will have achieved sexual satisfaction (4)

20 Changing sexual partners, especially within a large group (8)

21 French orgasm – and that's final! (5,4)

22 The pinnacle of sexual thrills (6)

23 Despicable fellow who trades in female flesh (4)

24 Stick your finger in one of these and she wont thank you for it, even if you are in Holland (4)

25 Father's little blue helper (6)

DOWN

1 Erotic tome you kept in that little lacquer box used as headrest (6,4)

3 Area of pigmented skin around the human nipple (6)

4 One of our first Scarlet Library titles – and a gentle art, I'm told (9)

5 Hamlet's ghastly pun for the female parts (7,7)

6 Madonna's book in the silver foil wrapper (3)

7 Fellatio etiquette does not insist upon this final act of disposal. Gulp! (7)

8 Chap who sells his posterior assets in Piccadilly (4,3)

11 Slang word meaning fellatio (3)

12 Woman writing erotica for a dollar a page in 30s and 40s Paris (3)

14 He goes on top but not to proselytise (10)

15 Keeping it in the family, so to speak (6)

16 Will Bob hold on to his penthouse? (8)

18 A high-five up yours! (7)

19 Small furry dam-builder which also inhabits ladies' knickers (6)

Beauty depends on size as well as symmetry.
No very small animal can be beautiful, for
looking at it takes so small a portion of time
that the impression of it will be confused.
Nor can any very large one, for a whole
view of it cannot be had at once, and so
there will be no unity and completeness.

Aristotle

SIZE
IS EVERYTHING

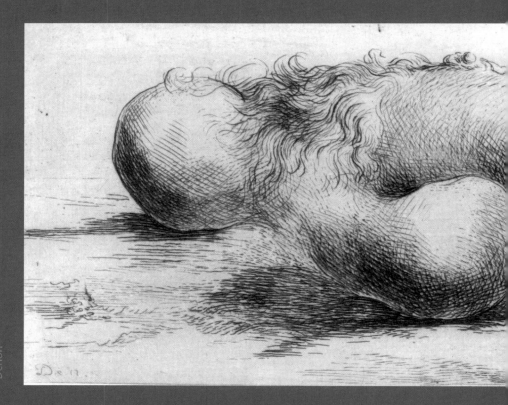

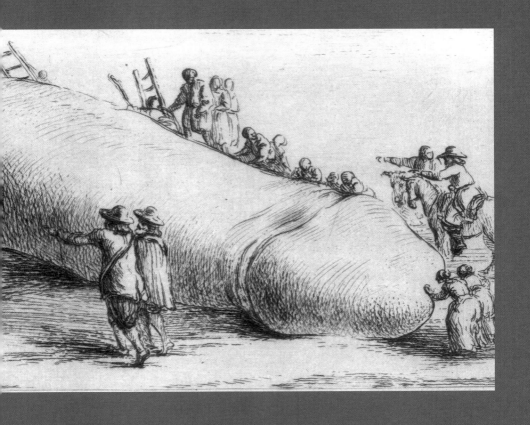

Pipifax

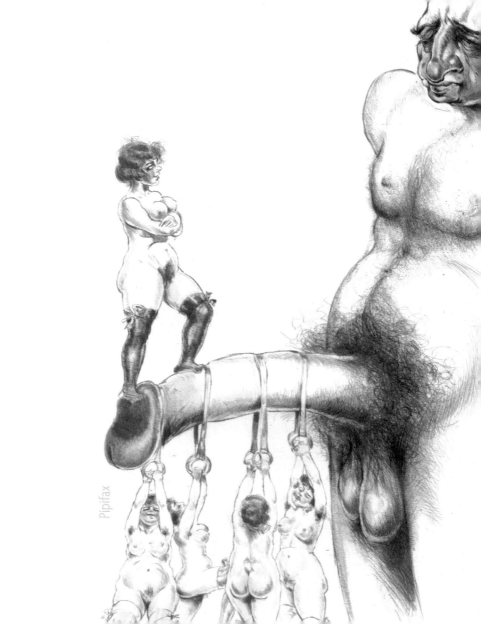

Pipifax

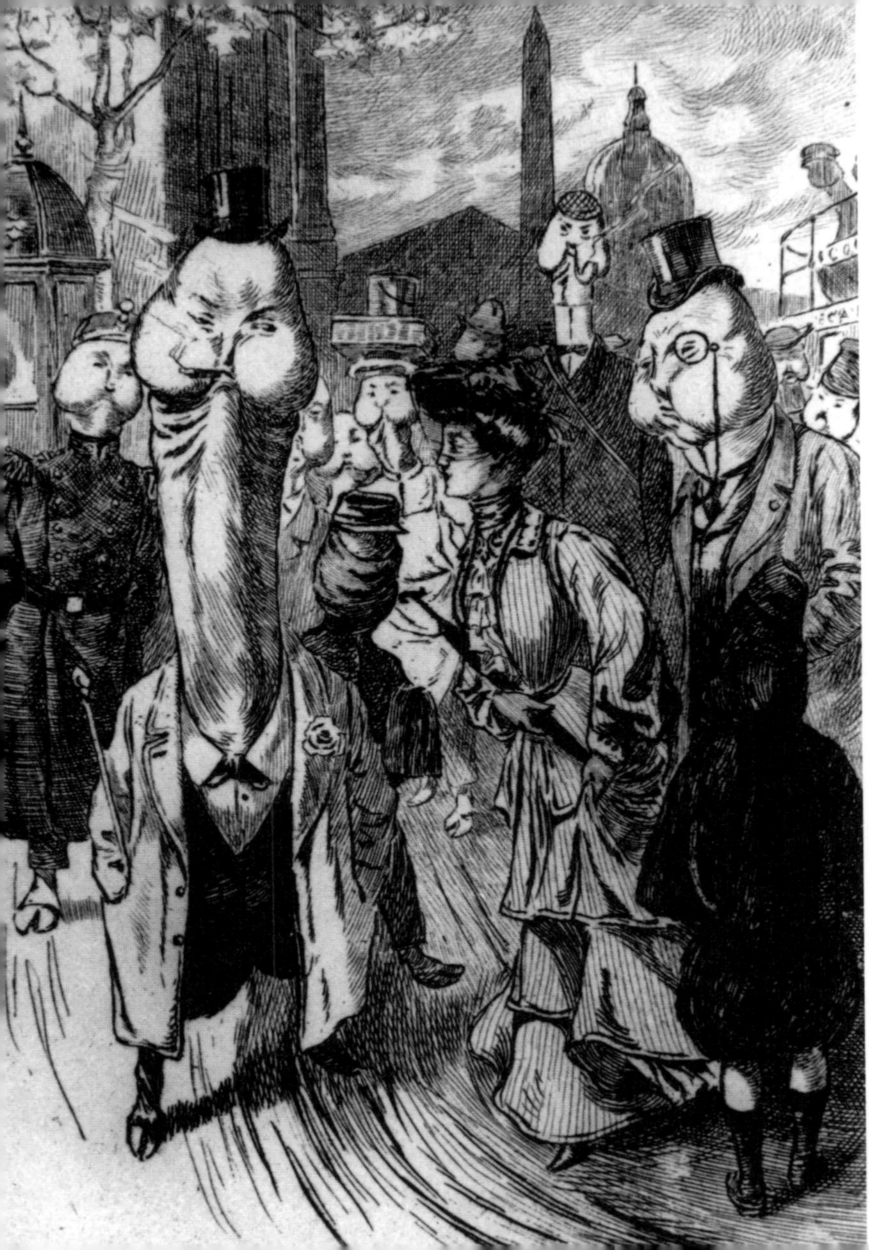

Van Maele

LYSISTRATA.

Sex between a man and a woman
can be absolutely wonderful –
provided you get between the
right man and the right woman.

Woody Allen

Best of Both Worlds

Best of Both Worlds

Kate Copstick

Whenever someone asks me to define my sexuality nowadays, I always get a flashback to a September night I spent in an overpriced London hotel room, with nothing on except a Rocco Siffredi DVD and my gorgeous black strap-on. I was buggering a boy called John whom I had picked up in a gay bar.

Somehow it felt much more natural (feel free to disagree) to use my ersatz inches to part the buttocks of this, admittedly, somewhat less than macho young man than to plunge it into the pinker parts of a woman. But where, I mused as I thrusted and plunged until the fronts of my thighs slapped the backs of his, did that leave me on the colour chart of sexuality?

The accepted choice for a girl is simplistic...

Heterosexual – which is like being in Alba in autumn and never eating truffles?

Lesbian – which is like gagging for a cup of tea in Tokyo and having to go through the entire bloody tea ceremony before you can get one?

Or bisexual – which is like living in London and being able to have anything you want and order it in to boot?

I have always been with Sir Laurence on the 'snails and oysters' question... I like both. So I am self-evidently bisexual. But what kind of bisexual am I? The question had occurred to me in the hotel room when the lovely and very obliging John turned the strap-on on me.

I do have problems with some aspects of bisexuality.

Women, mainly.

Don't get me wrong – I adore women. The first 'whole body' sexual experience I had was with a female. Fifteen and led entirely by instinct, my tongue found its way from her mouth, in a direct line down the openings in her clothing, to its natural home between her legs. I can remember the taste and the sensation still. Sweet and musky softness under a fuzz of soft new-grown hair. And her breasts – both soft and firm, like two little clenched iron fists in velvet gloves. A perfect handful each.

And the women I have had since – young women with neat, sweet, pink, rosebud cunts that need nibbling and licking like little buttered corncobs and older women with lush, louche, peony-rose cunts... the kind of ripe watermelon cunt you can lose almost your entire face in – each can erect my clit with just her memory.

In France I even found I enjoyed fat female flesh (well, my New Year's Resolution that year had been to try, each month, something I had never done before and, after February's 'first', at the Singles' Dinner, nothing frightened me) when the kind of woman whom Rubens would have asked to lose weight approached me round the back of a bus (yes, I could just tell the difference). There is something sexy about that much flesh on a female. All those curves, all that smoothness. A body to spread oneself across instead of wrapping oneself around. At the risk of sounding Oedipal – a huge motherfucker. Great breasts that spill over hands like seven pounds of prime meat in a bag and yet, still, a cute, pert-lipped, two-finger cunt. Like finding a sweetie in a duvet.

Yes, all my lips quiver at the thought of a woman.

But – and I am a butt girl – when I want an honest to goodness, goosepimple erecting, eyewatering fuck then I have to have a man.

Even a woman with a strap-on doesn't do it, despite having the kind of erection only naturally available with a mindless adolescent attached.

It is partly the power thing. Fucking is not a caring activity. People don't fuck. Bodies do. And arguably only bits of bodies do. I want a great big hard cock in my cunt... or ass... I do NOT want 'you inside me'. I want to be used. I will get embarrassed if you murmur my name. I want to be a sex object.

And women – generally – have a basic problem with objectification.

Men, on the other hand...

Like Julie Andrews, when I'm feeling sad, I simply remember my favourite things... the frighteningly right wing chap I met in the Groucho Club when both of us were dining with someone else. He murmured the magic words 'You have a great ass' as I passed his table for a second time. A bottle of champagne later, I was in a shoulder stand and North Clapham while he sank his dick into me like a pestle pounding into a mortar while chanting 'fuck you fuck you fuck you'... the theatre technician who walked into my dressing room, announced: 'I really want to fuck you' and had me on my hands and knees and in full Red Queen regalia in front of the "mirror mirror on my wall"... the gloriously endowed gentleman I met in the Lounge Car of the overnight train from Glasgow to London and in whose Executive First compartment I enjoyed seconds, thirds and got more cock in my mouth than a fox in a poultry farm... a wonderfully athletic American whose catchphrase was 'shut up bitch and open your mouth'.

I have only once had impersonal, body-bruising, pure-driven sex with a woman. She bit me, she chewed on my pussy... she played KitKat with my ass (that's four fingers...) Oddly, she thought she was straight. Not that night.

But I digress ... ok, 'deviate' is arguably *le mot juste*...

Quickies. Women have an underdeveloped appreciation of the quickie. The stand-up, no names, no talking, itch-scratching, thirst-quenching fuck. When I am horny and I just want my cunt or my ass filled and fucked and finished off. I have generally found it to be men that will do that for me. I once had in my life a fabulous man amongst whose many, many fine points was his habit of saying – as we reached the front door *en route* to cinema, restaurant or theatre: 'Fancy a quickie before we go?'

I have never had a woman like that.

I am well aware that a bit of girl-on-girl action is what feeds the fantasies of most heterosexual men. But, let's face it chaps, you don't think that girl-girl play is sex: it is just very pretty foreplay. But nothing like the real thing. It needs a man to complete it, right? Wrong.

Although I have to admit to some great threesomes.

But the woman has to be genuinely bisexual. Samantha was. And she had the great advantage of the callousness of the eighteen-year-old.

We met at a party, collected a *prima facie* alpha male and made for the master bedroom where he greeted the conversing quartet there with the immortal words, 'We're going to have sex now, you can stay if you want'. They didn't. Maybe that was pretty close to perfect... a cock in my ass and a pussy in my face. And an unspoken agreement that the exchange of body fluids need not lead to an exchange of phone numbers.

I think that that, for me, is the factor. I can't say whether sex with men or sex with women is better. They are so different. Sex with women makes me come... maybe even more than sex with men. But what I hate is that women always CARE that I've come.

The best sex is pure sex. Not sex complicated by emotion, by history, by personalities, by caring. Just sex.

And that seems to take a man.

ps Any woman who would like to prove me wrong, please contact EPS and ask for my number.

I want a great big hard cock in my cunt... or ass... I want to be a sex object.

Best of Both Worlds

Love in action is a harsh and
dreadful thing, as compared
with love in dreams.

Fyodor Dostoevsky

Nuns in Their Twats

Nuns in their Twats Dr. Christopher Hart

She turns up at ten to nine, immaculately timed, just as he is beginning to get jumpy but comfortably before he begins to get irritated. She slips between the groups of people standing at the bar and comes over to him. She is wearing a very plain, charcoal-grey cashmere dress, a black suede jacket and black suede pumps with modest heels. Bare brown legs, despite the chill November night. Her hair done up loosely on top with a little silk scarf. He has observed at least two men watching her as she crosses the bar.

What'll you have?

Vodka with ice she says. Oh, make it a double. What the hell, it's Friday night.

My pleasure, he thinks evilly. He buys her drink and rejoins her on the sofa. She sits cross-legged and half-turned towards him. This is the best bit, he thinks suddenly. Nothing else beats this: this moment. Nothing.

As the evening wears on she becomes more and more animated, her eyes glittering, her eyelids half-closed, looking so directly at him, and something in her expression that seems to him pointed and meaningful, loaded with significance.

You are mad, he says. A mad girl. Let's talk about you: interestingly mad you. It's a funny thing. I still don't feel I really know anything about you.

That's OK, she says. Neither do I.

There you go, he says, that's what I mean. He is laughing but he means it seriously. I mean, where did you grow up? Where did you go to school?

Hampshire.

And what sort of school?

She thinks for a short while and then says, A Reformatory.

Really?

Oh yes. She lays one hand on his knee. I was a very naughty girl.

How naughty? he asks provocatively.

Very naughty, she says. I was at a Reformatory run by nuns, for the Very Naughtiest Girls in England. And they were the Little Sisters of Discipline and Stern Reproof.

Stern... ? he says, going goggle-eyed.

Reproof she repeats, patting him on the knee again. And Discipline. Very strict they were, too. Any little breach of the rules and you were severely punished. You were only allowed to walk, not run, down the Marble Corridor, for instance, on the way to 4am Matins, no matter how late you were.

And you were caught running?

Oh no, I was caught flying. Well, not really flying, but certainly floating down the corridor, a couple of feet off the floor. But Sister Felicita was furious. She said she had never encountered anything so impertinent since her days as a foreman on a building site. And I had to be severely punished.

Go on, he says.

Well, I was taken to the Mother Superior's study, and there the Mother

Superior and Sister Felicita and Sister Perpetua made me bend down across the leather-topped desk...

Yes?

She sighs coyly. And... well, they made me hitch up my little gymslip.

You wore gymslips? That doesn't seem a very good idea for a Reformatory for Very Naughty Girls.

Little gymslips, she stresses. Very short they were. She plucks up the hem of her dress until it covers only the very upper reaches of her thighs, and she looks at him wide-eyed. That short at least, she says. She pulls it down again demurely. Oh, it was to put temptation in our way, she explains. We were always being told that the world was such a terribly wicked place, and before we were released back into society, we had to learn to be able to resist temptation. That was also the reason why all girls had to share double or even triple beds in communal dormitories, right up to the sixth form. And why the school uniform was always so deliberately... well, so skimpy, and sexy: gymslips, black stockings, high-heeled shoes, blouses that had to have at least the top four buttons undone at all times. And at bed-time, these really short, lacy nighties. And all the walls of our dormitories were decorated with these enormous, and most inflammatory murals depicting acts of... well...

Well?

She lowers her eyes to her feet and plays little-girlishly with the hem of her dress. Well, she whispers. Sapphic love.

He swallows. When he speaks his voice is hoarse.

Go on, he says, with a certain, undignified desperation.

And all the bedside cupboards had... well, you know... things in them.

Things?

Things, she repeats solemnly. Anyway, the day I was caught floating down the Marble Corridor, I was made to bend over this leather-topped desk, and hitch my little gymslip up around my waist. And then... actually, I wouldn't mind another drink, would you?

He looks around with wild impatience, unseeing, and says OK then, and takes the proffered note from her and buys a couple more drinks and returns in remarkably quick time. She is sitting back looking very relaxed and smoking a cigarette. She has been musing on how ridiculously easy it is to turn men on, how predictable their tastes are in erotic tales. And yet how she loves doing it. And this particular man, she admits, is very sweet: the rueful, apologetic smile, the awkward hand movements, the inarticulate mumblings.

Well? he says.

Oh, thank you darling, she says, leaning forward for her glass and taking a sip.

No, I mean... well?

Well what?

The spanking, the spanking! he hisses.

She looks at him blankly for a moment and then laughs and touches him on the arm. Oh I'm sorry, I'd quite forgotten. Now where was I?

Over the leather-topped desk, he says. Your gymslip up around your waist.

Quite so, she says, drawing deeply on her cigarette. You have been paying attention, haven't you?

I'm... I'm interested. From a purely, urm... erotico-philosophical point of view.

She eyes him with amusement as he sits there, on the edge of his seat, twitching at every cruel flick of her narrative whip. Well, she resumes. There I was, with my very short, tight gymslip hitched right up. And Sister Felicita started to spank me on the bottom with her bare hand. But after a while she stopped and said to the Mother Superior, I'm afraid that young Miss Elizabeth is a particularly recalcitrant young lady. I suggest that she requires chastisement on her bare flesh. The Mother Superior gave her assent, and so Sister Felicita and Sister Perpetua promptly positioned themselves either side of me and ordered me to part my legs a little. Then I felt two pairs of hands pulling my knickers down to my ankles. Then they both started spanking me again at the same time, on my bare buttocks.

Did it hurt?

Hm, sort of, she says dreamily. It's not an entirely unpleasant sensation, though. Like when you lie out in the sunshine naked and your bottom gets sunburned. And then after that they told me to stay where I was while they rubbed some cream into my skin to soothe it.

Then... then what?

That's... that's it. They told me to put my clothes back on and be off to lessons.

Oh, he says, disappointed.

You sound disappointed.

No, not at all. I just... I just thought it might get more...

Men! she tuts. You're all the same. You only ever think of one thing.

No, that's not true! he protests. I love fantasies and the build-up and all that bit. But in the end... well, you want the Happy Ending, don't you? You don't want to be left in the lurch.

Hm, she says, circling her fingertip round the rim of her glass (already empty again) and looking steadily at him. I don't know. I like the fantasy bit just as much. And you don't have to feel so guilty. After all, it's not actually doing it, is it?

No. No. It's not actually doing it, he agrees. So... so you mean, just, like fantasising with each other is OK, as long as it doesn't go any further?

I can't see anything wrong with it, can you?

No, nothing at all.

They have two more drinks before closing time and then rise to leave.

I'll get a cab in Fulham Road, she says.

Oh, I'll walk you, he says. Save you the cab fare.

Are you sure?

Of course I'm sure, he says, taking her gently but firmly by the arm. And anyway, he adds, when I get you home I intend to whisk you inside and up to your bedroom and fuck you senseless all night long. Though purely in fantasy, of course. I can't see anything wrong with that, can you?

How very rude, she says, and then smiles. Come on, then.

This short story first appeared in The Erotic Review

If one is prepared to chomp away in the time it takes to listen to an episode of *The Archers,* then swallowing at the grand finale isn't really much of a hardship, although I do think that *just* swallowing is proof enough of affection, there's no need to start showing off by gargling or blowing cum-bubbles, that's all a bit Thai prostitute if you ask me.

Annie Blinkhorn Oral Sex

ORAL
TRADITION

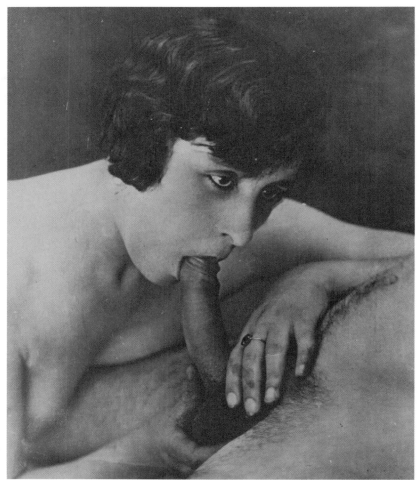

Anonymous

Anonymous

Rojan

Rojan

Rojan

St André

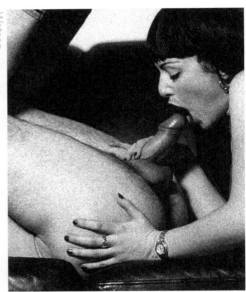

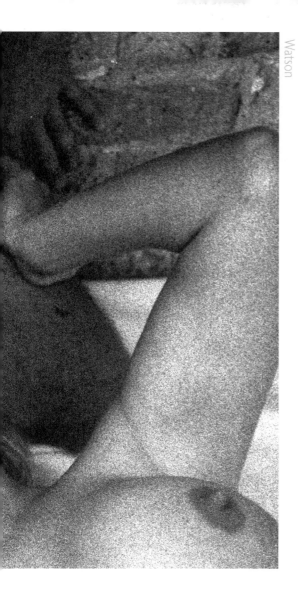

The merry month of May has always been famous for its propitious influence over the voluptuous senses of the fairer sex...

Sub-Umbra

or

sport amongst the

she-noodles

Foreword Dr. Christopher Hart

In the heady, creative heyday of late Victorian erotica, there were three magazines that stood proud: *The Cremorne*, *The Boudoir*, and *The Pearl*, the latter published between 1879 and 1880. 'For the extremes of pornography there is nothing quite the equal of these magazines,' writes Ronald Pearsall in his great study of underground Victorian sexuality, *The Worm in the Bud* (Macmillan, 1969).

They contained explicit illustrations, frequently betraying a truly dire standard of draughtsmanship, of the kind which can nevertheless have a peculiar, awkward charm for the connoisseur, their clumsiness evoking a world diametrically opposed to the air-brushed, silicon-enhanced images to be found on today's sterilised, homogenised and terminally humourless internet. The magazines also ran episodic stories, jokes, parodic hymns (very Victorian), verses and limericks; although in whichever genre, the time-honoured *vice anglais* of hearty spanking was always prominent. They were fantastically expensive for the time (*The Boudoir* cost fifteen shillings per 32-page issue), and none of them lasted for long.

The Pearl was the outstanding title in this unholy trinity, its title page declaring it to be a 'Monthly Journal of Facetiae and Voluptuous Reading,' and alleging, with just that same ponderous facetiousness, that it was printed at the Oxford University Press. It is from the pages of *The Pearl* this particular story, originally serialised, is taken. It ran under the glorious title, *Sub-Umbra, or Sport Amongst the She-Noodles*. As the publisher of this fine new edition has commented, this is a title so surreal as to be verging on the hallucinogenic. What on earth are she-noodles? Eric Partridge's great *Dictionary of Historical Slang* is no help here. The only definition he can give for 'noodle' is 'a simpleton, ca. 1750.' But surely the unknown author of the work cannot have been so unchivalrous as to describe his putative female partners as simpletons? I guess we can surmise something along the lines of 'schoolgirl strumpet,' judging from its content.

The plot is rudimentary, as always. The nineteen-year-old narrator goes to visit his cousins for a month down in Sussex. The cousins are Frank, also aged nineteen, and his three sisters, Annie, Sophie and Polly, aged eighteen, sixteen and fifteen. They flirt, banter, dally, very quickly have a great deal of sex in various combinations and, er... that's it. But it does make for a tremendously entertaining read.

The age of the girls involved in these multiple couplings can make the modern reader feel more than a little uncomfortable. But it is important to realise that the Victorian gentleman reader of such material would not have shared our concerns. For one thing, during much of the nineteenth century the age of consent was twelve, as it still is today in some Continental countries; and, as Pearsall sharply points out, the central idea of the Victorian wedding night was the almost ritualised defloration of a virgin bride. And whether your partner was your wife or a Haymarket whore, as a gentleman you would always have to pay. The liberating sense in so much Victorian erotica, as evident in *Amongst the She-Noodles* as anywhere, is that all the febrile fornication so vividly described has nothing to do with a bourgeois exchange of cash or property, but is indulged in by the females, as well as by the males, for the sheer Joy of Sex.

It is something of a truism nowadays that in mainstream Victorian literature, the very notion of female sexual desire was utterly taboo, above all in Dickens; although some sense of female passion, at least, does appear in the Brontës, George Eliot, and surprisingly perhaps, in Trollope. However, for a straightforward depiction of female desire, arousal, rapture and satiation, such as we would now find in the literary fiction of Jeanette Winterson, say, or Angela Carter, the only place to look in the nineteenth century is pornography.

No one would claim any literary status for *Amongst the She-Noodles*. The writing style has the same clumsy charm and incongruity as *The Pearl*'s illustrations. One of my favourite examples occurs after the narrator and Frank have simultaneously savoured the delights of another teenage friend, Miss Rosa Redquim (the names might make you wince, but are all part of the period charm).

"'I say, old fellow,'" he exclaimed, "'by Jove! it's quite impossible for me to wait till tomorrow for the chance of enjoying that delicious Rosa... no no, it must be this very night if I die for it!'"

Later, the narrator gets a taste for slightly older women, in the voluptuous shape of Colonel Leslie's wife: 'young and gay... a beautiful brunette of about three-and-twenty.' Soon enough they are panting and gasping in each other's arms, and Mrs Leslie is burdened with such lines as: 'You rogue, you young villain, your kisses and touches have undone me... Ah! What a naughty, impatient boy, to come so quickly! Pull off your clothes, sir, and let us take our fill of love on yonder bed!'

There are several more conquests to come, including the young Misses Bruce, Emily and Louisa, aged fifteen and fourteen respectively, and like all the other fantasy females here: 'impatiently awaiting their immolation to the god of love with open legs and longing cunts.'

Perhaps the most original element of *Amongst the She-Noodles* is the scene in which the narrator briefly digresses to enjoy the charms of a He-Noodle: cousin Frank himself. '"Ha! Ha! Ha!"' are the narrator's words of seduction, 'laying my hand upon his cock. "By Jove, Frank! What a tosser yours has grown into since we used to play in bed together a long time ago."'

For all its preposterous and dated air, there is still something highly entertaining about *Amongst the She-Noodles*; it has its moments of genuine eroticism, and when not quite managing to scale the erotic heights, it can be very funny. Sometimes it even manages to be sexy and funny at the same time. And who could ask for more than that?

Sub Umbra or Sport Amongst the she-noodles Anonymous

Illustrated by Sylvie Jones

The merry month of May has always been famous for its propitious influence over the voluptuous senses of the fairer sex.

I will tell you two or three little incidents which occurred to me in May 1878, when I went to visit my cousins in Sussex, or as I familiarly call them, the 'she-noodles', for the sport they afforded me at various times.

My uncle's is a nice country residence, standing in large grounds of its own, and surrounded by small fields of arable and pasture land, interspersed by numerous interesting copses, through which run footpaths and shady walks, where you are not likely to meet anyone in a month. I shall not trouble my readers with the name of the locality, or they may go pleasure hunting for themselves. Well, to go on, these cousins consisted of Annie, Sophie and Polly, beside their brother Frank, who, at nineteen, was the eldest, the girls being, respectively, eighteen, sixteen and fifteen. After dinner on the first day of my arrival, Paterfamilias and Mama indulged in a snooze in their armchairs, whilst we boys and girls (I was the same age as Frank) took a stroll in the grounds. I attached myself more particularly to cousin Annie, a finely developed blonde with deep blue eyes, pouting red lips and a full heaving bosom, which to me looked like a perfect volcano of smothered desires. Frank was a very indolent fellow who loved to smoke his cigar, and expected his sisters, who adored him, to sit by his side, reading some of the novels of the day, or tell him their love secrets, &c. This was by far too tame an amusement for me, and as I had not been there for nearly three years, I asked Annie to show me the improvements in the grounds before we went in to tea, saying to Frank, banteringly, 'I suppose, old fellow, you're too lazy, and would prefer your sister to take me round?'

'I'm too comfortable. Lazy is an ugly word, Walter, but the fact is, Soph is just reading me a most interesting book, and I can't leave it,' he replied. 'Besides, sissie is quite as well or better qualified than I am to show off the grounds. I never notice anything.'

'Come on, Annie,' said I, taking her hand, 'Frank is in love.'

'No, I'm sure he never thinks of a girl, except his sisters,' was the reply.

We were now out of earshot, in a shady walk, so I went on a little more freely. 'But surely you, coz, are in love, if he is not. I can tell it by your liquid eye and heaving bosom.'

A scarlet flush shot over her features at my allusion to her finely moulded bosom, but it was evidently pleasing, and far from offensive, to judge by her playfully spoken: 'Oh! Walter, for shame, sir!'

We were a good distance away by this time, and a convenient seat stood near so, throwing my arms around the blushing girl, I kissed her ruby lips, and drawing her to me, said, 'Now, Annie, dear, I'm your cousin and old playfellow. I couldn't help kissing those beautiful lips, which I could always make free with when we were little boy and girl together; now you shall confess all before I let you go.'

'But I've nothing to confess, sir.'

'Do you never think of love, Annie? Look me in the face if you can say it's a stranger to your bosom,' putting my hand familiarly round her neck till my right hand rested on one of the panting globes of her bosom.

She turned her face to mine, suffused as it was by a deeper blush than ever, and her dark blue eyes met mine in a fearless search of my meaning. Instead of speaking in response to this mute appeal, I kissed her rapturously, sucking in the fragrance of her sweet breath till she fairly trembled with emotion.

It was just beginning to get dusk, and my hands were caressing the white, firm flesh of her beautiful neck, slowly working their way a little lower towards the heaving bubbies. At last I whispered, 'What a fine bust you have developed since I saw you last, dear Annie. You won't mind your cousin, will you, when everything used to be so free to each other? Besides, what harm can there be in it?'

She seemed on fire, a thrill of emotion seeming to shoot

through both of us, and for several moments she lay almost motionless in my arms, with one hand resting on my thigh. Priapus was awake and ready for business, but she suddenly roused herself, saying, 'We must never stop here. Let us walk round or they will suspect something.'

'When shall we be alone again, darling? We must arrange that before we go in,' I said quickly.

It was impossible to keep her on the seat, but as we walked on she said musingly, 'Tomorrow morning we might go for a stroll before lunch. Frank lies in bed, and my sisters are keeping house this week; I shall have to mind the tarts and pies next week.'

I gave her another hug and a kiss, as I said, 'How delightful that will be! What a dear, thoughtful girl you are, Annie.'

'Mind, sir, how you behave tomorrow, not so much kissing, or I shan't take you for a second walk. Here we are at the house.'

Next morning was gloriously warm and fine. As soon as breakfast was over we started for our stroll, being particularly reminded by Papa to be back in good time for luncheon.

I gradually drew out my beautiful cousin, till our conversation got exceedingly warm, the hot blood rushing in waves of crimson over her shame-faced visage.

'What a rude boy you have grown, Walter, since you were here last. I can't help blushing at the way you run on, sir!' she exclaimed at last.

'Annie, my darling,' I replied. 'What can be more pleasing than to talk of fun with pretty girls, of the beauties of their legs and bosoms, and all about them? How I should love to see your lovely calf at this moment, especially after the glimpses I have already had of your divine ankle,' saying which I threw myself under a shady tree, close by a gate in a meadow, and drew the half-resisting girl down on the grass at my side, and kissed her passionately, murmuring, 'Oh! Annie, what is there worth living for like the sweets of love?'

Her lips met mine in a fiery embrace, but suddenly disengaging herself, her eyes cast down, and looking awfully abashed, she stammered out, 'What is it? What do you mean, Walter?'

'Ah, coz dear, can you be so innocent? Feel here the dart of love all impatient to enter the mossy grotto between your thighs,' I whispered, placing her hand upon my prick, which I had quickly let out of the restraining trousers. 'How you sigh! Grasp it in your hand, dear, is it possible that you do not understand what it is for?'

Her face was crimson to the roots of her hair as her hand grasped my tool, and her eyes seemed to start with terror at the sudden apparition of my cock. Taking advantage of her speechless confusion, my own hand, slipping under her clothes, soon had possession of her mount, and in spite of the nervous contraction of her thighs, the forefinger searched out the virgin clitoris.

'Ah! oh! oh! Walter, don't; what are you about?'

'It's all love, dear, open your thighs a wee bit and see what pleasure my finger will make you experience,' I again whispered, smothering her with renewed and luscious kisses and thrusting the velvet tip of my tongue between her lips.

'Oh! oh! you will hurt!' she seemed to sigh rather than speak, as her legs relaxed a little of their spasmodic contraction.

My lips continued glued to hers, our otherwise disengaged arms clasped each other closely round the waist and her hand held my prick in a kind of convulsive grasp whilst my fingers were busy with clitoris and cunny. The only audible sound resembled a mixture of kisses and sighs, till all in a moment I felt her crack deluged with a warm, creamy spend whilst my own juice spurted over her hand and dress in loving sympathy.

In a short while we recovered our composure a little, and I then explained to her that the melting ecstasy she had just felt was only a slight foretaste of the joy I could give her by inserting my member in her cunny. My persuasive eloquence and the warmth of her desires soon overcame all maiden fears and scruples. Then, for fear of damaging her dress, or getting the green stain of the grass on the knees of my light trousers, I persuaded her to stand up by the gate and allow me to enter her from behind. She hid her face in her hands on the top rail of the gate, as I slowly raised her dress. What glories were unfolded to view: my prick's stiffness was renewed in an instant at the sight of her delicious buttocks, so beautifully complemented by the white of her pretty drawers. As I opened them and exposed the flesh, I could see the lips of her plump, pouting cunny, deliciously feathered with soft, light down, her lovely legs, drawers, stockings and pretty boots making a *tout ensemble*, which as I write and describe them cause my prick to swell in my breeches – it was a most delicious sight. I knelt and kissed her bottom, slit and everything my tongue could reach. Standing up, I prepared to take possession of the seat of love when, alas! a sudden shriek came from Annie, her clothes dropped and all my

arrangements were upset in a moment; a bull had unexpectedly appeared on the opposite side of the gate, and frightened my love by the sudden application of his cold, damp nose to her forehead. It is too much to contemplate that scene even now.

Annie was ready to faint as she screamed, 'Walter! Walter! Save me from the horrid beast!' I comforted and reassured her as well as I was able, and seeing that we were on the safe side of the gate, a few loving kisses soon set her right. We continued our walk, and soon, spying out a favourable shady spot, I said, 'Come, Annie dear, let us sit down and recover from the startling interruption. I am sure, dear, that you must still feel very agitated. Besides, I must get you now to compensate me for the rude disappointment.'

She seemed to know that her hour had come; the hot blushes swept in crimson waves across her lovely face as she cast down her eyes, and permitted me to draw her down by my side on a mossy knoll, and we lay side by side, my lips glued to hers in a most ardent embrace.

'Annie! Oh, Annie!' I gasped. 'Give me the tip of your tongue, love.' She tipped me the velvet without the slightest hesitation, drawing, at the same time, what seemed a deep sigh of delightful anticipation as she yielded to my slightest wish. I had one arm under her head, and with the other I gently removed her hat, kissing and sucking at her delicious tongue all the while. Then I placed one of her hands on my ready cock, which was in bursting state, saying, as I released her tongue for a moment: 'There, Annie, take the dart of love in your hand.' She grasped it nervously, as she softly murmured, 'Oh, Walter, I'm so afraid, and yet – oh, dearest, I feel, I die, I must taste the sweets of love, this forbidden fruit,' her voice sinking almost to a whisper, as she pressed and passed her hand up and down my shaft. My hand was also busy finding its way under her clothes as I again glued my mouth to hers, and sucked at her tongue till I could feel her vibrate all over with the excess of her emotion. My hand, which had taken possession of the seat of bliss, was fairly deluged with her warm, glutinous spendings.

'My love, my life! I must kiss you there, and taste the nectar of love,' I exclaimed, as I snatched my lips from hers, and reversing my position, buried my face between her unresisting thighs. I licked up the luscious spendings with rapturous delight from the lips of her tight little cunny, then my tongue found its way further, till it tickled her sensitive clitoris and put her into a frenzy of mad desire for still further enjoyment. She twisted her legs over my head, squeezing my head between her firm, plump thighs in an ecstasy of delight.

Wetting my finger in her luscious crack, I easily inserted it in her beautifully wrinkled, brown bum-hole, and keeping my tongue busy in titillating the stiff little clitoris, I worked her up into such a furious state of desire that she clutched my cock and brought it to her mouth, as I lay over her to give her the chance of doing so. She rolled her tongue round the purple head, and I could also feel the loving, playful bite of her pearly teeth. It was the acme of erotic enjoyment. She came again in another luscious flood of spendings, whilst she eagerly swallowed every drop of my sperm as it burst from my excited prick.

We both nearly fainted from the excess of our emotions, and lay quite exhausted for a few moments, till I felt her dear lips again pressing and sucking my engine of love. The effect was electric; I was as stiff as ever.

'Now, darling, for the real stroke of love,' I exclaimed, shifting my position, and parting her quivering thighs, so that I could kneel between them. My knees were placed upon her skirts so as to preserve them from the grass stain. She lay before me in a delightful state of anticipation, her beautiful face all blushes of shame, the closed eyelids fringed with their long, dark lashes, her lips slightly open and the finely-developed, firm, plump globes of her bosom heaving in a state of tumultuous excitement. It was ravishing. I felt mad with lust, and could no longer put off the actual consummation. I could not contain myself. Alas, poor maidenhead! Alas, for her virginity! I brought my cock to the charge, pushing the head just slightly between the lips of her vagina. A shudder of delight seemed to pass through her frame at the touch of my weapon as her eyes opened, and she whispered, with a soft, loving smile, 'I know it will hurt, but Walter, dear Walter, be both firm and kind. I must have it, if it kills me.' Throwing her arms around my neck, she drew my lips to hers, as she thrust her tongue into my mouth with all the abandon of love, and shoved up her bottom to meet my charge.

I had placed one hand under her buttocks, whilst, with the other, I kept my prick straight to the mark. Then, pushing vigorously, the head entered about an inch, till it was pressing hard against the opposing hymen. She gave a start of pain, but her eyes gazed into mine with a most encouraging look.

'Throw your legs over my back, my dear,' I gasped, scarcely relinquishing her tongue for a moment. Her lovely thighs came round me in a spasmodic frenzy of determination to bear the worst. I gave a ruthless push, just as her bottom heaved up to meet me, and the deed was done. King Priapus had burst through all obstacles to our enjoyment. She gave a subdued shriek of agonised pain, and I felt myself throbbing in possession of her inmost charms.

'You darling! You love me! My brave Annie, how well you stood the pain. Let us lie still for a moment or two, and then for the joys of love,' I exclaimed, as I kissed her face, forehead, eyes and mouth in a transport of delight at feeling the victory so soon accomplished.

Presently I could feel the tight sheath of her vagina contracting on my cock in the most delicious manner. This challenge was too much for my impetuous steed. He gave a gentle thrust. I could see by the spasm of pain which passed over her beautiful face that it was still painful to her so, restraining my ardour, I worked very gently; but my lust was so maddening that I could not restrain a copious spend and I sank on her bosom in love's delicious lethargy.

It was only for a few moments. I could feel her tremble beneath me with voluptuous ardour, and the sheath being now well lubricated, we commenced a delightful bout of ecstatic fucking. All her pain was forgotten, and the wounded parts, having been soothed by the flow of my semen, now only revelled in the delightful friction of love. She seemed to boil over in spendings, and my delighted cock revelled in it as he thrust in and out with all my manly vigour. We spent three or four times in a delirium of voluptuousness till I was fairly vanquished by her impetuosity, and begged her to be moderate, and not to injure herself by excessive enjoyment.

'Oh! can it be possible to hurt oneself by such a delightful pleasure?' she sighed, then seeing me withdraw my limp tool from her still longing cunt, she smiled archly, as she said with a blush, 'Pardon my rudeness, dear Walter, but I fear it is you who are most injured after all; look at your bloodstained affair.'

'You lovely little simpleton,' I said, kissing her rapturously. 'That's your own virgin blood; let me wipe you, darling,' as I gently applied my handkerchief to her pouting slit, and afterwards to my own cock. 'This, dearest Annie, I shall treasure up as the proof of your virgin love, so delightfully surrendered to me this day,' exhibiting the ensanguined *mouchoir* to her gaze.

We now rose from our soft, mossy bed, and mutually assisted each other to remove all traces of our love engagement.

Then we walked on, and I enlightened the dear girl as to all the arts and practices of love. 'Do you think,' I remarked, 'that your sisters or Frank have any idea of what the joys of love are like?'

'I believe they would enter into it as ardently as I do, if they were but once initiated,' she replied. 'I have often heard Frank say when kissing us, that we made him burn all over'. Then, blushing deeply as her eyes met mine, she said 'Oh, dear Walter, I'm afraid you will think we are awfully rude girls, but when we go to bed at night, my sisters and I often compare our budding charms, and crack little jokes about our developing slits, and the young pussy of Polly. We have such games of slapping, and romps too, sometimes; it has often made me feel a kind of all-overishness of feverish excitement I could not understand, but thanks to you, love, I can make it all out now; I wish you could only get a peep at us, dear.'

'Perhaps it might be managed. You know my room is next to yours, and I could hear you laughing and having a game last night.'

'I know we did, we had such fun,' she replied. 'It was Polly trying to put my pussy in curl papers, but how can you manage to watch us, dear?'

Seeing she fully entered into my plans for enjoyment, we consulted together, and at last I hit upon an idea which I thought might work very well. It was that I should first sound out Frank and enlighten him a little in the ways of love, and then as soon as he was ripe for our purpose, we would surprise the three sisters whilst bathing naked, and slap their naked bottoms all round. Annie was to encourage her sisters to help in tearing off all our clothes, and then we could indulge in a general romp of love.

Annie was delighted at the idea, and I promised the very next day to begin with Frank, or perhaps that very afternoon if I got a chance.

We returned to the house, Annie's cheeks blushing and carrying a beautiful flush of health, so that her Mama remarked that our walk had evidently done her very great good, little guessing that her daughter, like our first mother Eve, had that morning tasted of the forbidden fruit, and was greatly enlightened and enlivened thereby.

After luncheon I asked Frank to smoke a cigarette in my room, which he at once complied with.

As soon as I had closed the door, I said, 'Old fellow, did you ever see *Fanny Hill*, a beautiful book of love and pleasure?'

'What, a smutty book, I suppose you mean? No, Walter, but if you have got it I should very much like to look at it,' he said, his eyes sparkling with animation.

'Here it is, my boy, only I hope it won't excite you too much. You can look it over by yourself, as I read *The Times*,' said I, taking it out of my dressing-case, and handing it to his eager grasp.

He sat close to me in an easy lounging chair, and I watched him narrowly as he turned over the pages and gloated over the beautiful plates. His prick hardened in his breeches till it was quite stiff and rampant.

'Ha! Ha! Ha! Old fellow, I thought it would fetch you out!' I said, laying my hand upon his cock. 'By Jove, Frank! What a tosser yours has grown into since we used to play in bed together a long time ago. I'll lock the door and we must compare our parts – I think mine is nearly as big as yours.'

He made no remark, but I could see he was greatly excited by the book. Having locked the door, I leant over his shoulder and made my remarks about the plates as he turned them over. At length the book dropped from his hands, and his excited gaze was riveted on my bursting breeches. 'Why, Walter, you are as bad as I am,' he said, with a laugh. 'Let's see which is the biggest,' pulling out his hard, stiff prick, and then laying his hands on me and pulling my cock out to look at.

We handled each other in an ecstasy of delight, which ended in our throwing off all our clothes, and having a mutual fuck between our thighs on the bed. We spent in rapture, and after a long dalliance he entered into my plans, and we determined to have a lark with the girls as soon as we could get a chance. Of course I kept mum as to what had passed between Annie and myself.

In the course of the evening, Frank and I were delighted by the arrival of a beautiful young lady of sixteen, on a visit to his sisters, in fact a school-fellow of Sophie and Polly, who had come to stop a week at the house.

Miss Rosa Redquim was indeed a sprightly beauty of the Venus height, well-proportioned in leg and limb, with a full, swelling bosom and a graceful, Grecian type of face, rosy cheeks, large grey eyes, golden auburn hair, lips as red as cherries and teeth like pearls, frequently exhibited by a succession of winning smiles, which never seemed to leave her face. Such was the acquisition to the feminine department of the house, and we congratulated ourselves on the increased prospect of sport, as Frank had expressed to me considerable compunction as to taking liberties with one's own sisters.

The next morning being gloriously fine and warm, myself and Frank strolled in the grounds, smoking our cigarettes, for about an hour, till near the time when we guessed the girls would be coming for a bathe in the small lake in the park, which we at once proceeded to. Then we secreted ourselves secure from observation, and awaited, in deep silence, the arrival of sisters and friend.

This lake, as I call it, was a pond about four or five acres in extent, every side thickly wooded to the very margin, so that even anglers could not get access to the bank, except at the little sloping green sward, of about twenty or thirty square yards in extent, which had a large hut, or summer-house, under the trees; here the bathers could undress, and then trip across the lawn to the water. The bottom of the pond was gradually shelving, and covered with fine sand at this spot, and a circular space was enclosed with rails, to prevent them from getting out of their depth.

The back door of the hut opened upon a very narrow footpath leading to the house through the dense thicket, so that any party would feel quite secure from observation. The interior was comfortably furnished with seats and loungers, as well as a buffet, which generally held a stock of wine, biscuits and cakes during the bathing season.

Frank, having a key to the hut, took me through to the lawn, and then climbing up into a thick sycamore, we re-lit our cigarettes, awaiting the adventure with some justifiable impatience.

Some ten minutes of suspense, and then we were rewarded by hearing the ringing laughter of the approaching girls. We heard the key turn in the lock then the sounds of their bolting themselves in, and Annie's voice, saying, 'Ah! Wouldn't the boys like the fun of seeing us undress and bathing on this lovely warm day', to which we heard Rosa laughingly reply, 'I don't mind if they do see me, if I don't know it, dears. There's something delightful in the thought of the excitement it would put the dear fellows in. I know I should like Frank to take a fancy to me; I'm nearly in love with him already, and have read that the best way a girl can madly excite the man she wishes to win is to let him see all her charms, when he thinks she is unconscious of his being near.'

'Well, there's no fear of our being seen here, so I am one for a good romp. Off with your clothes, quick; it will be delicious in the water,' exclaimed Sophie.

The undressing was soon accomplished, excepting chemises, boots, and stockings, as they were evidently in no hurry to enter the water.

'Now,' said Sophie, with a gay laugh, 'we must make Rosa a free woman, and examine all she's got. Come on, girls, lay her down, and turn up her smock.'

The beautiful girl only made a slight feint of resisting, as she playfully pulled up their chemises, exclaiming, 'You shan't look at my fanny for nothing. What a pretty pouting slit yours is, Annie. I think you have been using the finger of a glove we made into a little cock for Sophie, and told her to bring home from school for you.'

She was soon stretched on her back on the soft mossy grass, her face covered with burning blushes, as her pretty cunt was exposed to view, ornamented with its *chevelure* of soft, red hair; her beautiful, white belly and thighs shining like marble in the bright sunlight. The three sisters were blushing as well as their friend, and delighted at the sight of so much loveliness.

One after another, they kissed the vermilion lips of their friend's delightful slit, and then turning her on her face, proceeded to smack the lily-white bottom of their laughing, screaming victim, with open hands.

Smacks and laughter echoed through the grove, and we almost fancied ourselves witnesses to the games of real nymphs. At last she was allowed to rise on her knees, and then the three sisters in turn presented their cunts to their friend to kiss. Polly was the last, and Rosa, clasping her arms firmly round my youngest cousin's buttocks, exclaimed, 'Ah! Ah! You have made me feel so rude, I must suck this little jewel,' as she glued her lips to it, and hid her face almost from sight, as if she would devour Polly's charms there and then. The young girl, flushed with excitement, placed her hands on Rosa's head, as if to keep her there, whilst both Annie and Sophie, kneeling down by the side of their friend, began to caress her cunt, bosom and every charm they could tickle or handle.

This exciting scene lasted for five or six minutes, till at last they all sank down in a confused heap on the grass, kissing and fingering in mad excitement.

Now was our time. We had each provided ourselves with little switches of twigs, and thus armed we seemed to drop from the clouds upon the surprised girls, who screamed in fright and hid their blushing faces in their hands.

They were too astonished and alarmed to jump up, but we soon commenced to bring them to their senses, and convince them of the reality of the situation.

'What rude, lascivious ideas! Slash away, Frank!' I cried, making my swish leave its marks on their bottoms at every cut.

'Who would have thought it, Walter? We must whip such indecent ideas out of their tails!' he answered, seconding my assault with his sharp, rapid strokes.

They screamed both from pain and shame, and springing to their feet, chased round the lawn, but there was no escape. We caught them by the tails of their chemises, which we lifted up to enable us to cut at their bums with more effect. At last we were getting out of breath, and beginning fairly to pant from exhaustion, when Annie suddenly turned upon me, saying, 'Come, come, girls, let's tear their clothes off, so they shall be quite as ashamed as we are, and agree to keep our secret!' The others helped her, and we made such a feeble resistance that we were soon reduced to the same state in which we had surprised them, making them blush and look very shamefaced at the sight of our rampant engines of love.

Frank seized Miss Redquim round the waist, and led the way into the summer-house, myself and his sisters following. We gentlemen then producing the wine, &c., from the buffet, sat down with a young lady on each knee, my friend having Rosa and Polly, whilst Annie and Sophie sat with me. We plied the girls with several glasses of champagne each, which they seemed to swallow in order to drown their sense of shame. We could feel their bodies quiver with emotion as they reclined upon our necks, their hands and ours groping under shirts and chemises in every forbidden spot. Each of us had two delicate hands caressing our cocks, two delicious arms around our necks, two faces laid cheek to cheek on either side, two sets of lips to kiss, two pairs of bright and humid eyes to return our ardent glances; what wonder then that we flooded their hands with our spurting seed and felt their delicious spendings trickle over our busy fingers.

Excited by the wine, and madly lustful to enjoy the dear girls to the utmost, I stretched Sophie's legs wide apart, and sinking on my knees, gamahuched her virgin cunt, till she spent again in ecstasy, whilst dear Annie was doing the same to me, sucking the last drop of spend from my gushing prick. Meanwhile Frank was following my example, as Rosa surrendered to his lascivious tongue all the recesses of her virginity as she screamed with delight and pressed his head towards her mount when the frenzy of love brought her to the spending point, Polly all the while kissing her brother's belly, and frigging him to a delicious emission.

When we recovered a little from this exciting *pas de trois*, all bashfulness vanished between us, and we promised to renew our pleasures on the morrow, making ourselves, for the present, content with bathing all together, and then returning to the house for fear the girls might be suspected of something wrong for staying out too long.

After luncheon Frank smoked his cigarette in my room; the events of the morning had left both of us in a most unsettled and excited state.

'I say, old fellow,' he exclaimed. 'By Jove! It's quite impossible for me to wait till tomorrow for the chance of enjoying that delicious Rosa; besides, when there are so many of us together there is just the chance of being disappointed. No, no, it must be this very night if I die for it; her room is only the other side of my sisters'.'

I tried to persuade him from doing anything rashly, as we could not yet be certain that, even excited and ready as she had shown herself, she was prepared to surrender her virginity so quickly. However, arguments and reasonings were in vain. 'See,' he exclaimed. 'The very thought of her makes my prick ready to burst,' opening his trousers and letting out his beautiful red-headed cock as it stood in all its manly glory, stiff and hard as marble, with the

hot blood looking ready to burst from his distended veins. The sight was too exciting for me to restrain myself, the cigarette dropped from my lips, and going upon my knees in front of him, I kissed, sucked, frigged and played with his delicious prick till he spent in my mouth with an exclamation of rapture and I eagerly swallowed every drop of his copious emission. When we had recovered our serenity a little, we discussed the best plans for the night, as I was determined to have my share of the amusement, which Frank most willingly agreed to, provided he was to go first to Rosa's room, and prevail upon her to consent to his ardent suit. Then, when all seemed to be *en règle*, I was to surprise them in the midst of their fun, and join in the erotic frolic.

After dinner we adjourned to the drawing-room, where a most pleasant evening was enlivened by music and singing, leaving Frank turning over the leaves for Rosa and Polly, as they sang 'What Are the Wild Waves Saying?' Annie and Sophie whispered to me that they should like a short stroll in the garden by moonlight, so opening the window, we stepped out on to the path, where we could walk with an almost noiseless tread. Papa and Mama were in the library playing cribbage, and we felt sure that

Frank and Rosa would not run after us, so passing rapidly down a shady walk, with one arm round each of the dear girls' waists, and alternately kissing one and then the other, I followed the instinct of love which allowed me to guide the willing girls into a rather dark arbour without the least demur on their part.

'How lovely the honeysuckle smells!' sighed Sophie, as I drew them both down by my side in the corner, and began a most delicious kissing and groping in the dim obscurity.

'Not so sweet as your dear little pussy,' said I, playfully twisting my fingers in the soft down around the tight little grotto of love which I had taken possession of.

'Oh! Oh! Mind, Walter dear!' she sighed softly, as she clung round my neck.

'Will you let me kiss it as I did Annie's this morning, my little pet? It will give you such pleasure and there's nothing to be bashful or shamefaced about here in the dark – ask your sister if it wasn't delicious.'

Annie urged her sister on, saying, 'Oh! let him, Sophie dear, you will experience the most heavenly sensations.'

Thus urged she allowed me to raise her clothes, and recline her backwards in the corner, but this would not admit of Annie having her fair share of the game. As she was now all aflame with excited expectation, there was no difficulty in persuading her to kneel over my face as I reclined on my back at full length on the seat; lovely hands at once let my eager prick out of his confined position in my trousers, and as I commenced to suck and gamahuche Sophie, I felt that the dear Annie had taken possession of my cock for her own special benefit.

'Oh! let me kiss you, Sophie dear, put your tongue in my mouth,' said Annie, straddling me, and putting my excited engine of love up her own longing crack, and beginning a delightful St George. I clasped the younger girl firmly round the buttocks with one arm, whilst with my right hand I found and rubbed her stiff little clitoris to increase her excitement from the lascivious motions of my tongue in her virgin cunny.

Annie was in a frenzy of voluptuous enjoyment as she bounced up and down on my prick, now and then resting for a moment to indulge in the exquisite pleasure of the devil's bite, which she seemed to possess to a most precocious extent, the folds of her cunt contracting and throbbing upon my swelling prick in the most delicious manner.

Sophie was all of a tremble, wriggling herself most excitedly over my mouth, and I licked up her virgin spendings as they came down in a thick creamy emission.

'Oh! Oh! Oh!' she sighed, hugging and kissing Annie in fondest abandon. 'What is it, dear? I shall choke, Walter. There's something running from me; it's so delicious. Oh! What shall I do?'

Annie and I met at this moment in a joint spend, which left us in an ecstatic lethargy of love, and the two sisters almost fainted upon my prostrate body. When we had recovered a little, I sat up between the loving sisters.

Sophie, throwing her arms round my neck, quite smothered me with her burning kisses, as she whispered in my ear, 'It was such pleasure, dear Walter. Is that one of the delights of love, and what was Annie doing, for she was excited as I was?'

'Can't you guess, darling?' I replied, taking her hand and placing it upon my still rampant cock. 'That is what she played with.'

'But how?' whispered the innocent girl. 'She was kissing and sucking my tongue deliciously all the while, but seemed as if she could not keep still a moment.'

'She had that plaything of mine up her cunny, my dear, and was riding up and down upon it till we all fainted with pleasure at the same time. You shall have a real lesson in love next time, and Annie won't be jealous, will you, dearest?'

Annie replied 'No, no, we must all be free to enjoy all the games of love without jealousy. I wonder how Frank is getting on with Rosa by this time. We must now make haste back to the house.'

Sophie was anxious for more explanations as to the arts of love, but was put off till another time. All being now in a cooler state of mind, we returned to the house, where we found Frank repeating the game of the morning, by gamahuching Rosa, whilst Polly was gone out of the room.

The red-haired beauty was covered with blushes, as she suddenly dropped her clothes on our entrance, and only recovered from her crimson shamefacedness when Annie laughingly assured her that we had been enjoying ourselves in the same manner.

'Oh! How rude and indecent of us all,' exclaimed Rosa, 'but who can resist the burning touches of a handsome young fellow like your brother. He was so impudent, but it sends such a thrill of voluptuousness through the whole frame.' With this, she commenced to sing 'It's Naughty, But It's Nice'.

The supper bell rang and, after a light repast, we all separated to our rooms. Frank came into my chamber to join in a cigarette and a glass of grog before finally retiring.

'It's all right for tonight, old fellow,' he exclaimed, as soon as we were seated for our smoke. 'I begged Rosa to let me kiss all her charms, in her own room without the inconvenience of clothes. She made some objections at first, but finally consented not to lock the door if I promised not to go beyond kissing, on my honour as a gentleman.'

He was too impatient to stop long, and, after only one smoke, cut off to his room. Undressing myself as quickly as possible, I went to him, and escorted him to the door of his lady-love; it was unlocked, and he glided noiselessly into the darkened chamber. She was evidently awake and expecting his visit, for I could hear their rapturous kissing and his exclamation of delight as he ran his hands over her beautiful figure.

'My love, I must light the candles to feast my eyes upon your extraordinary beauties. Why did you put out the lights?' She made some faint remonstrances, but the room was soon a blaze of light from half-a-dozen candles.

I was looking through the keyhole, and eagerly listening to every word.

'My love, let us lie side by side and enjoy feeling our bodies in naked contact before we begin kissing each other's charms.'

I could see that his shirt and her *chemise de nuit* were both turned up as high as possible, and his prick was throbbing against her belly. He made her grasp it in her hand, and pulling one of her legs over his thighs, was trying to place the head of his eager cock to the mark between her legs.

'Ah! No! No! Never! You promised on your honour, sir!' she almost screamed in alarm, struggling to disengage herself from his strong embrace. 'No! No! Oh! No! I won't, indeed!'

His previous soft manner seemed in a moment to have changed to a mad fury, as he suddenly rolled her over on her back, keeping his own legs well between her thighs.

'Honour! Honour!' he laughed. 'How can I have honour when you tempt me so, Rosa? You have driven me mad by the liberties I have been allowed. Resistance is useless. I would rather die than not have you now, you dear girl.'

She struggled in desperate silence for a few moments, but her strength was unequal to his; he gradually got into position, and then taking advantage of her exhaustion, rapidly and ruthlessly completed her ravishment.

She seemed insensible at first, and I took advantage of her short unconsciousness to steal into the room, and kneel at the foot of the bed, where I had a fine view of his bloodstained weapon thrusting in and out of her shattered virginity. After a little she seemed to begin to enjoy his movements, especially after the first lubricating injection of his love-juice. Her buttocks heaved up to meet his thrusts, and her arms clung convulsively round his body, seeming reluctant to let him withdraw, until both seemed to come together in a luscious spend.

As they lay exhausted after this bout, I advanced and kissed the dear girl, and as she opened her eyes, I placed my hand across her mouth to stop any inconvenient scream of surprise. I congratulated her on having so nicely got rid of her troublesome virginity, and claimed my share of the fun, drawing her attention to the rampant condition of my cock in contrast to Frank's limp affair. I could see she was now eager for a repetition of the pleasure she had only just begun to taste. Her eyes were full of ardent desire as I placed her hand upon my prick.

In accordance with our previously devised arrangements she was persuaded to ride a St George upon me. My cock was inserted in her still tender cunt with great care, and allowed slowly to get into position, but the excitement was too great for me and with an exclamation of delight I shot a stream of sperm up into her very entrails. This set her off and she began slowly to move upon me, her cunt gripping and throbbing upon the shaft most deliciously, and we were soon running another delightful course. This was too much for Frank, for his cock was again as hard as iron and eager to get in somewhere, so kneeling up behind her he tried to insert his prick in her cunt alongside of mine, but found it too difficult to achieve. then the charming, wrinkled orifice of her pink bottom-hole caught his attention, and as the tip of his cock was wet with our spendings, his vigorous shoves soon gained an entrance. I was holding her fast and she was too excited to resist anything, only giving a slight scream as she found him slip inside of the part she thought was only made for another purpose. I asked them to rest a few moments and enjoy the sensation of feeling where we were, our pricks throbbing against each other in a most delicious manner, with only the thin membrane of the anal canal between them. It made us spend immediately to the great delight of Rosa, who at once urged us to go on.

This was the most delightful bout of fucking I had ever had; she made us do it over and over again and, when we were exhausted, sucked our pricks up to renewed cockstands. This lasted till the dawn of day warned us of the necessity of precaution, and we retired to our respective rooms.

Next morning Annie and her sisters rallied us upon our late appearance at the breakfast table, remarking with a pouting look that we could not care much for their company if we lay a-bed and left them to themselves for the best half of the day, and that Rosa was just as bad, for she was actually still in dishabille, taking her breakfast in her own room.

Here Mama interposed, adding, 'Besides, Walter, I am astonished you should copy Frank's lazy ways, you who on your first arrival here were so eager for early-morning walks. Look at Annie, she is not half so rosy and animated as she looked after your first walk.'

A deep flush passed across Annie's face at this allusion to our first eventful walk, when we had the adventure with the bull, but I prevented her parents from observing it by replying that residents in town were always in such a hurry to enjoy the fresh air, and that it seemed to have an extraordinary somnolescent effect upon me, as I could hardly keep my eyes open at supper time, or rouse myself from sleep in the morning.

Frank said 'I'm glad you have found out it is not all laziness now. Walter will take my part when I assert it is the natural drowsiness of youth, which is readily induced by the keen bracing air we breathe all day.'

Papa made a few incredulous, ironical remarks about the youth of the present day, and then breakfast being over, as he rose from the table, said, 'Walter, would you mind riding a dozen miles to oblige me? Frank would not be ready to start for an hour at least; besides, I would rather trust you than him with the lady my note is for. Colonel Leslie's wife is both young and gay, and I would rather not run the risk of Frank being one day a co-respondent in the Divorce Court, and I caution you to take care of yourself.'

I readily assented, more especially when I noticed a shade of jealous anxiety flit across Annie's face. The horse was already at the door, so springing into the saddle I rode off with a fluttering anticipation of something racy being likely to turn up. I shall not recount my reflections during this delightful hour's ride. The atmosphere was most deliciously bracing, and my thoughts were so amorously bent that when I reined up at the lodge-gate at the entrance to the colonel's grounds, I felt that I could fuck anything in petticoats, from a witch to a gatepost. The gatekeeper soon passed me in, and I dismounted from my saddle before the door of a fine old Elizabethan hall. My knock was promptly responded to by a most handsome, young, coloured fellow with a Hindu cast of feature.

Mrs Leslie was at home, and he begged I would excuse her from coming down to the drawing-room, as she was still at her toilette, and would immediately see me in her private boudoir.

This courteous message revived all my romantically amorous ideas with which I had indulged myself during my ride.

Ushered into the boudoir, I found the lady of the house to be a beautiful brunette of about three-and-twenty with a most bewitching expression of countenance, whilst her large, full, dark eyes seemed to read my very soul as she extended her hand and drew me to a seat by her side, saying, 'So, you are cousin Walter, I suppose. How is it that Frank did not ride over with his papa's note? But tell him,' she added with a very arch look, 'that I was quite as well pleased to see you, and that I consider his cousin quite as fascinating as himself.'

Then, ringing the bell, she continued, 'Will you take a cup of chocolate with me after your ride? It will invigorate me for the serious business of your uncle's note,' opening a drawer and laying several bundles of papers like legal documents on the table, just as the servant entered (he was the good-looking Hindu who had first introduced me).

Mrs Leslie said, 'Vishnu, bring up the chocolate, with two cups and some biscuits, and mind not to forget the flask of *noyau*,' remarking to me as he disappeared, 'Is he not a good-looking heathen? The colonel had him long before he married me, and I call him his principal Hindu deity. Whenever I look at him it puts me in mind of Joseph and Potiphar's wife, especially now the colonel is away; do you not think it a burning shame to leave a young wife all alone by herself?'

She continued to run on in this curious way, without giving me a chance to make a reply or observation in return, as she busied herself laying out the papers, making pretence of an awful lot of business to be gone through

The servant now brought in the chocolate, &c., and was dismissed with the order to tell Annette that her mistress would be busy for some time, and was not to be disturbed until she rang for the completion of her toilette.

My fair hostess was a most charming object as she moved about in her dressing-gown, which was rather open at the neck, so as to display the upper part of the snowy prominences of her luscious bosom, besides which I caught glimpses of her naked feet, with nothing on but the most *petite* blue satin slippers.

Presently she poured out two cups of chocolate, put in a little of the *noyau*, and presenting me with one of them took her seat by my side on the soft, yielding sofa. 'Drink it off as I do,' she said. 'It will do you far more good than sipping it and allowing it to get cold.'

We both drank our small cups at a draught, and I almost instantly felt a thrill of voluptuous warmth rush through my frame, and looking at my fair companion, saw that her eyes seemed to sparkle with a strange, amorous fire.

The devil was in me; in less time than it takes to write it, my empty cup was put on the table, and my disengaged arm placed round her neck. I drew her face to mine, and imprinted several kisses on her lips and cheeks as my other hand took possession of that inviting bosom; she was covered with blushes as she exclaimed, 'Fie! Fie, sir! How can you take such liberties when I can't help myself without dropping my cup?'

'Dear lady, excuse my liberties, and don't distress yourself. I am really greatly obliged to the cup for its assistance, for how can I look upon such loveliness without being tempted, yes, tempted! I am driven mad by the sight of such charms; you will excuse, you will pardon my presumption, I am sure,' I ejaculated, throwing myself upon my knees before her and hiding my face in her lap, as I clasped my arms nervously round her waist and felt her whole frame tremble with emotion.

Suddenly she seemed to start with pain as she exclaimed, 'Ah! Goodness! Oh! Oh! Oh! The cramp in my legs. Oh! Oh!' as the cup was thrown down by her side. 'Oh, release me, sir! Oh, Walter, excuse me, I must rub it!'

Here was a splendid opportunity to improve a lucky chance. 'Permit me, poor, dear lady, you are in such dreadful pain, and I am a medical student,' I said, making bold to raise her dressing-gown and chafe her lovely calves with my eager hands. What lovely legs I now beheld, with not a vestige of anything on them. My blood was on fire, as my fingers gradually wandered higher and higher, and I could not refrain from imprinting kisses on the delicious, soft, pinky flesh, as she seemed rather to sigh than speak, 'Oh! Thank you, pray don't, it's so indelicate, and the cramp is gone now.'

'No, no, dear Madame, the nervous contractions of your beautiful thighs convince me that it is higher up, and will return again in a few moments unless I can relieve you; indeed, you must not mind me, as I am a medical man,' I quickly replied, making bolder advances every moment, and taking advantage of the warm temperament I knew she possessed.

'You rogue, you young villain, your touches and kisses have undone me; how can I resist a handsome student? Oh, Walter, Walter, I must have you! I had only been trying to draw you out a little, never thinking you were such a young gallant, and now I am caught in my own net!

'Ah! What a hurry. You'll spoil it all by your impetuosity; you shall never have me without first kissing the shrine of love.

'Sir!' pushing me away, as I was endeavouring to get between her lovely thighs. 'Strip, strip, sir, I must see my Adonis, as your Venus now unveils herself to you.' Throwing off her dressing-gown (which I now saw was her only article of clothing), and drawing my face down to hers, she thrust her tongue into my mouth, 'tipping the velvet' in the most delicious style of voluptuous abandon, and delightfully handling my prick and balls at the same time. It was too much for my impatient steed, and my spendings flew all over her hands and body almost instantly.

'Ah! What a naughty, impatient boy, to come so quickly! Pull off your clothes, sir, and let us take our fill of love on yonder bed. My husband deserves this, for leaving me open to such temptation. You dear boy, how I shall love you! What a fine prick you have, and so... so... what do they call it? – (blushing at her own words) so randy! That's what the colonel says of the young fellows. Isn't it a dreadfully rude word, Walter? But so full of meaning. Whenever he said so, I couldn't help wishing for a handsome, randy young gentleman, such as your uncle has sent me today.'

This is how she ran on, as I threw off everything, and I was as naked as herself in a trice. Then, hugging and kissing, belly to belly, and handling each other's charms in every possible way, we slowly progressed towards the inviting bed in the other room. Once or twice I stopped and tried to get my prick into her standing up, but she would have none of that, and at last, when her bottom rested against the edge of the bed, she ordered me to kneel down and kiss the seat of love. How my tongue searched out her fine, stiff clitoris, which projected quite an inch and a half from the lips of her vagina. I sucked it in ecstasy, and titillated her sensitive organs so that she spent profusely in a minute or two, holding my head with her hands to make me go on. It was a most deliciously enjoyable gamahuche and my tongue revelled in her creamy emission, till she begged me to slip off my shirt, come on the bed and let her enjoy

my fine prick. So I ended this prelude with a playful, loving bite on her excited clitoris, and then, springing to my feet, rolled with her onto the bed, her ready hand grasping my cock as I mounted her lovely body.

'What a shame!' she sighed. 'The way you have been spending, you naughty boy, you won't have much left for me now... but he's fine and stiff!' as she squeezed it in her hand, and brought the head of my prick to the mark.

I found her deliciously tight, and assured her she was quite a virgin.

'So I should be, my dear Walter, but for you. The colonel has got so little to please me with that, tight as I am, I can hardly feel him, but now your jewel of pleasure makes me feel gorged with delight!'

Her motions were as lascivious as her words. She writhed and threw up her buttocks with extraordinary rapidity and energy, whilst I was equally eager and rapid in ramming into her delicious cunt.

I was as ready as if I had never spent, and we swam in a mutual emission almost immediately, both of us being so overcome by our feelings that we almost swooned in delight. This only lasted for a minute for the throbbing and contracting of the folds of her vagina on my enraptured prick awoke me to renewed efforts. We were rapidly progressing towards another spend, when she checked me, and begged I would withdraw for a little, when she would amuse me till she felt she must have him again. She added, 'I shall enjoy it so much more if I can make you last longer. Sit on my body, Walter dear, and lay your beautiful prick between the globes of my bosom; you shall spend there next time. I can't help telling you what a fine one it is, over and over again!'

She went on caressing it with her hand, and making her two bubbies close upon it, so that I could work between them. It was another delicious idea, but she had not exhausted all her ways of exciting me. Her other hand passed under my thigh, and I thought she was frigging herself, but it was only to wet her finger, preparatory to frigging my bottom-hole with it. This made me come again almost directly.

'Now,' said she, 'I mean to ride on you, and make it last as long as possible, so let us reverse positions.'

This was done, and she rode me and stopped alternately for about twenty minutes, when we met in a glorious flow of sperm.

'What do you think of that?' she exclaimed, as soon as she recovered her breath. 'We will get up and answer your uncle's letter now, and you shall promise to come again soon.'

Nothing of moment occurred during the evening, after my visit to Mrs Leslie, but I could see that Annie was rather piqued because I had nothing to tell her, except that I thought the colonel's lady a most charming person, and had been pressed to stay with her to luncheon before she would write a reply to my uncle's note.

Next day being the last representation of a celebrated piece at the theatre of the county town by a first-rate London company, Papa expressed a wish that we should all go in the evening, but Annie and Sophie, giving me a knowing look on the sly, declared they had already seen it once and did not care to go again. For my part, of course, I had seen it half a dozen times in town, so it was finally arranged that Frank, Rosa and Polly only would go with Papa and Mama. They had a drive of more than an hour before them, so started at 6 p.m., and as soon as they were out of sight we three started for the bathing place at the lake. It was a deliciously warm evening, and it would be just the place for our anticipated pleasures, as I had suggested to Annie and Sophie during the day.

Bolting the summer-house door on the inside as soon as we got in, I suggested first of all that we stimulate our mutually ardent desires with a bottle of champagne. This so exhilarated the two lovely girls that we indulged in a second bottle before stripping for a romp. Seven o'clock found us bathed in a flood of golden light from the declining sun, which now shone directly in upon us, warning us to make haste and improve the opportunity. Each one assisting the others and at the same time indulging in many loving tricks and liberties, we were soon in Adam and Eve costume.

'Now,' I exclaimed, 'Annie dear, you won't be jealous if I make a woman of your sister, as we promised the other day,' taking the younger one up in my arms with my rampant cock throbbing against her belly, as I carried her to the lounger.

'What a naughty boy you are, Walter. Anything or anybody for a change is what fickle men like, but I won't be jealous of Sophie, although I am of Mrs Leslie. I know you had her yesterday; that sheepish tell-tale look, sir, when you met me on your return, was enough to confirm my suspicions of what would happen when you were *tête-à-tête* with that killing lady,' she replied.

'For shame, Annie, darling, you told me yourself the other day love ought to be free everywhere. I don't deny my guilt, but will do my best to earn forgiveness now,' I said, pushing Sophie back upon the soft, yielding lounger. 'Help me to ease this darling of her troublesome virginity, and I will then repay your own longing cunny for all your love and forebearance. I am sure Mrs Leslie would like to make you one of our party without any feelings of jealousy; there are so many ways of voluptuous enjoyment that if there is only one man to three girls it can be so varied as to give everyone the most intense delight.'

At this both the girls gave me rapturous kisses, with every possible assurance that they never would be selfish, and would be only too happy to extend the circle of those they could be free and loving with, adding with special emphasis, 'We are such noodles, dear Walter, we knew nothing till you introduced us to the arts of love, and as long as you can stay with us we shall look to you to guide us in everything. We know it's wrong, but what heavenly pleasure there is in the loving mixture of the sexes.'

Annie, taking my prick in her hand, said 'Now, sir, I will show this gentleman the way into Sophie's cabinet of love. Be firm, dear, he won't hurt you more than can be helped, and the after-joy will soon drown all recollection of the first short suffering.'

Sophie, opening her legs as wide as possible replied 'I'm all on fire to taste the real tree of love. Don't spare me, Walter, dear, I'd rather die than not have it now!'

The red head of 'Cupid's Battering Ram' was now brought to the charge; Annie opened the rosy lips of her sister's cunt and placed my cock in the exact position, but her touches, together with the thoughts of the delicious titbit I was about to enjoy, caused me to spend in a moment all over her fingers and into the virgin passage in front. 'Push on, push on; now's the time to gain your victory.' She whispered; 'that will make it easier to get him in,' at the same time lifting up Sophie's buttocks with her disengaged hand, so as to make her meet my attack in a more favourable manner. My first lunge lodged the head of my prick fairly within the tight folds of the victim's vagina, and I had already won the first outworks of the virgin's defences.

Poor Sophie moaned under the sharp pain of my assault, but biting her lips to repress any cries of pain she courageously placed one hand on the shaft of my prick, as if jealous of her sister's loving help, and anxious to have the honour of herself showing me the way to achieve love's dearest triumph, or perhaps it was for fear of my withdrawing before completely accomplishing my task.

'You love!' I exclaimed, enraptured by this exhibition of pluck, 'I will soon make a real woman of you.' Then, pushing fiercely on, I gradually forced the tight sheath to dilate. Every obstruction gave way to my determined energy, and with a final plunge, I was buried to the roots of my cock, and shooting at the same moment my warm spendings into her inmost vitals. This exhausted me for a few moments, and I lay supine upon the heaving bosom of the lovely

Sophie, till I could feel Annie's fingers busy tickling my balls and feeling the shaft of my cock. Just at the same moment Sophie, who had almost fainted under the painful ordeal, opened her eyes, and with a loving smile pouted her lips as an invitation for a kiss, which I instantly responded to, almost sucking her breath away in my ardour. My excitement was now raised to the highest possible pitch by her sister's titillations, and the loving challenge of Sophie herself to renew my motions within her, by heaving up her bottom and nipping my prick in her cunny in the most delightful way imaginable.

This time I prolonged the pleasure as much as possible, beginning slowly, and often stopping to feel the delicious throbbings of cock and cunny in their delightful conjunction. 'Ach! this is indeed love; it repays for all the pain I felt at first. Oh! oh! dear Walter, it feels as if my very soul was flowing from me in ecstasy!' she almost screamed out, kissing, biting, squeezing me with all her might at the moment of emission, which I again responded to with a flow of my own sperm.

I now declared that we must refresh ourselves a little before going further, so she reluctantly allowed me to withdraw. A short plunge in the lake had a most invigorating effect. I felt as strong as a giant again and another bottle of fizz soon renewed our loving ardour as the girls were handling my prick, which stood again as hard as ivory. So slipping on my shirt, as I intended to be the uppermost of the trio, I laid Sophie on her back. Then, telling the obedient Annie to kneel over her sister and gamahuche her in return for Sophie's doing the same by her, I mounted up behind her, saying, 'I've made a woman of your dear sister, and will now treat you, my darling, to a new sensation.' But just at that moment Sophie, who had no idea of my intentions, seized hold of my cock, saying she must kiss the dear sweet thing which had afforded her such exquisite bliss. Holding it tight in her hand, she took the head between her pearly teeth and kissed and treated him to such love bites that I soon spent in her mouth, which she greedily swallowed with all the abandon of voluptuous enjoyment. Meanwhile, I had been frigging Annie's bottom with my two fingers, which I had managed to insert together, and that dear girl was sucking her sister's quim, and wriggling herself in the most excitable way possible.

Sophie was now going to insert my prick in her sister's cunt, but Annie, almost beside herself with excitement, exclaimed, 'No, no, my dear, put him where Walter has got his fingers for I should like to try that, it is so exciting; the very thought of it makes me mad with desire to know what it is like. His fingers have given me such pleasures that I am sure the dear thing in your hand will greatly improve the sensation!'

No sooner said than done; the obedient girl directed my cock to the beautifully wrinkled, tight, little brown hole of her sister's bottom at the very moment I withdrew my fingers. When I found they so thoroughly appreciated the idea I had resolved to initiate them into, and being well lubricated and as stiff as possible, I soon passed the portals of Annie's second virginity. But, Heavens, what a delicious bout we had; she bounded about so with delight that I had to hold tight round her neck to prevent being thrown out,

whilst Sophie, below, gamahuched her delighted sister, and with her right hand continued to press my balls and prick, keeping time to every insertion in her sister's bottom. We all spent together, almost screaming with delight, and then lay in a confused heap, enjoying all the sensations of our delicious exhaustion.

As soon as they could kiss and persuade my rather enervated tool into renewed stiffness, Sophie declared I must oblige her with a taste of the new-found joy, and ravish her bottom as well as her sister's.

This was another delicious love engagement, the sisters gamahuching each other with the utmost erotic ardour, whilst my delighted prick revelled in the tight-fitting fundament of the sweet girl, who wriggled and plunged about so excitedly that I had to hold fast to keep my place.

After this, we returned to the house, and passed the time very pleasantly till the return of the party from the theatre. I was anxious to hear Frank's account of how he had got on with Rosa during the evening, and especially as they drove home.

'Walter,' he said, as we were once more alone in his room after all had gone to rest, 'I've had a most enjoyable time of it since we started. Of course, when we left, it was daylight, so Rosa and I maintained a proper decorum, but at the theatre, Papa and Mama were separated from us by Polly, and we all five sat in the front row of the dress circle. The sight of Rosa's swelling bosom (which her low-necked dress allowed me fully to see) made my prick stand at attention, so I took her gloved hand and made her feel how hard and excited it was. As no one could see, she indulged me with quite a gentle frigging outside my trousers till I spent profusely, to the great delight of the roguish beauty, as I could tell by the smile on her face and the excited looks with which she met my ardent gaze.

' "What a shame," she whispered in my ear. "I know what you have done, you naughty boy. You should have reserved it for a more favourable opportunity."

' "Look out, darling, as we drive home; see if I don't repay your kind attentions," I whispered in return.

'Both Papa and Mama were rather sleepy before the conclusion of the last act, and to make them go off, as soon as we were seated in the carriage, I offered them my flask of brandy to keep out the effects of the night air. It had a good strong dose of narcotic in it, and they were soon sound asleep in their corners. Polly also pretended to be dozing.

'Rosa was on my lap directly, and my hands were at once groping their way to her seat of pleasure whilst she was equally busy unbuttoning my trousers and handling the staff of life.

'Our lips met in long-drawn rapturous kisses, which fired every drop of blood in our veins, and both of us were too impatient for the real business to prolong our toyings with each other's privates; besides, I felt she was already spending over my busy fingers. She had my cock in a glorious state of erection, so opening her delicious thighs as she raised her clothes, she at once impaled herself on the spike she so burned to have thrust into her. It was quite equal to the first time I fucked her. The long evening had passed in expectation of what I might be able to do on our return journey: it had so added to the piquancy of my arduous longings that I seemed in Heaven itself, and swimming in a very ocean of love, we spent over and over again. Our melting kisses and tongue-sucking continually stimulated us to renewed exertions, till the near approach to home warned us of the necessity of bringing our pleasures to an end for a time. Even now I tell you, Walter, my cock keeps throbbing and standing at the very thought of the delightful pressures she treated me to; her cunt bites so deliciously.'

In the morning, Papa and Mama had scarcely slept off the effects of the sleeping dose they had imbibed from the brandy flask of their dutiful son, and lay a-bed very late, in fact, almost to luncheon time. Meanwhile, we, the younger members of the family, had privately agreed upon a plan of amusement for the afternoon and evening.

Finding that two pretty young girls of fourteen and fifteen were living close by, with an invalid mother, whilst their brother was away, being a midshipman in the Royal Navy, I proposed that Annie should send the Misses Bruce an invitation to spend the afternoon with us, *en famille*, without the least ceremony, and join us in an *alfresco* tea party at a little hut in the woods, which formed part of my uncle's estate.

At luncheon we informed the governor of what we had done and hoped that both he and Mama would join in our outdoor party in the woods.

'No thank you, my dears, we are too afraid of the damp grass and rheumatics. Besides, we have not yet got over the fatigue of yesterday. We will stay quietly at home and hope you may enjoy yourselves thoroughly, as we should do if we were younger,' replied the jolly, kind-hearted old gentleman.

This was exactly what we had wished for and expected, so Frank and Annie at once sent off the servants with every requisite for our open-air tea party.

About three o'clock, the two young ladies arrived, and as all were ready, we at once set off for the scene of our anticipated fun, which was a rough bower covered with flowering honeysuckle and clematis, at the end of a long, shady, private walk, more than half a mile from the house.

Frank and myself particularly attached ourselves to the two fresh young ladies as being the greatest strangers, and therefore justly expectant of the most attention.

Emily Bruce, the elder, was a charming dark-eyed brunette, her rather large mouth having a fascinating effect as you regarded her. In fact, such a display of pearly-white teeth I never saw before, and the very thought that they might perhaps be soon employed in love bites on my tender-headed prick filled me with maddening lust to possess myself of their owner.

Nor was her sister, Louisa, any less prepossessing, she being almost the counterpart of Emily, except that one could easily see there was a slight difference in age.

When we arrived at the bower, the servants were at once sent home, being told that they could clear away the things next morning, as it would be too late for them to return in the evening. At the same time, without asking the consent of her young friends, dear Annie scribbled a pencil note to their mama, to say that if they were at all late, she would insist upon them staying with her all night, and not to make herself at all anxious on their behalf – this was quietly sent off by one of the servants.

As soon as we were alone, Frank and I, uncorking the champagne, lighted our cigars and, saying that the sun was still too warm for outdoor romping, pressed the girls to try some very mild cigarettes of Turkish tobacco.

At last Annie and Rosa set the example by lighting up, and were at once laughingly followed by the others. Our two young friends protested they never took wine. Still, they evidently sipped it with great delight, and we bantered them upon being so tied to their mother's apron strings, &c., till they began to be quite as free as my cousins and Rosa.

We had a good stock of fizz, besides sandwiches and cake, so that no one seemed at all anxious to take the trouble of tea-making.

Still we were careful that only enough should be taken to warm our friends up to a slightly excitable state, in fact, just to induce that state of all-overishness, which tingles through a young girl's sensitive frame when she feels the first vibrations of amorous desires, which she can as yet hardly understand.

Their sparkling eyes, slightly flushed faces and above all, the dazzling beauties of their teeth as they indulged in gay laughter at our *badinage*, set all of us aflame. I could see that Rosa and my cousins were longing to help in enjoying these innocent and ravishing young girls.

Now a game of 'hunt the slipper' was proposed, and we at once adjourned to the soft, mossy-green sward outside the bower. This was a most delicious and excitable romp.

Whenever it came to our turns, Frank and myself indulged in all kinds of quick and startling touches, which made the two little dears blush up to their eyes at first, and when we managed to catch one of them with the slipper we claimed a hearty kiss as penalty, which they submitted to with tolerable grace, yet evidently in a state of great excitement, as it was all so new to them. We finished the game, had a little more champagne, then proposed a game of hide-and-seek in the wood, with the reservation that no one was to go too far off.

We were to be in pairs. I chose Emily, and Frank took Louisa. Polly and Sophie went together, whilst Annie and Rosa had to search for us when we called out.

It so happened that there was an old sand-pit close by in which, several years before, Master Frank had amused himself by making a Robinson Crusoe's cave, and had planted bushes in front of it, so that the entrance was perfectly out of sight, and no one would fancy anyone could be screened by the small amount of cover which seemed to grow on the side of the pit. This was just the place for our purpose, and it had been arranged beforehand that we were not to be found for a long time. Gliding into the cave, Frank let fall the old curtain that hung at the entrance, and we were at once in the dark. The place was large enough for us all to sit together on a heap of fine soft sand at the further end.

'What a dear girl you are!' I whispered in Emily's ear, as I took a kiss in the dark, and drew her trembling body quite close by putting an arm around her waist. 'Pray, don't,' she whispered in return. 'If you do not keep quiet I won't stop in this dark place.'

'Don't say so; it would be cruel, especially if you knew all I feel towards you, Emily dear. I must call you Emily, yes, and kiss you again and again. I love you so, and your breath is so fragrant. What are you afraid of, there's nothing to fear among friends, darling,' I whispered, kissing my partner rapturously.

'Oh, ah, you take my breath away, Walter, I'm so unused to such goings-on. Oh, fie, sir, for shame, you make me feel all a-tremble, you take such liberties!' as I was working one hand inside the bosom of her dress, and getting possession of two hard, round bubbies which throbbed with emotion under my loving caresses.

'It's all love, darling, and no one can see, can't you hear how Frank and Louisa are kissing; is it not delicious to think they are doing the same, and will be sure to keep our secret?'

A deep sigh was my only answer, and again our lips met in a long luscious kiss. My tongue was thrust into her mouth, and tickled the tip of her own velvety organ of speech. I could feel the nipples of her virgin bosom stick out as stiff as little cocks and whispered to her to allow me to kiss them.

'I can refuse you nothing,' she whispered. 'You are such a bold lover. I'm all in flame from head to foot at the numberless liberties you are taking with me. Ah, if Mama only knew,' she sighed, as I was now sucking her titties and running my disengaged hand up her thighs. They were nipped tightly together, but gradually relaxed under the gentle pressure of my hand, till I actually got possession of her cunny, which I could feel was slightly covered with soft, downy hair, and soon began to frig her gently with my forefinger. The dear girl wriggled under this double excitement, and I could feel one of her hands groping outside my trousers over my bursting prick to return the pleasure I was giving her. One by one she unfastened the buttons, and her soft, delicate hand soon had possession of my stiff cock, naked and palpitating with unsatisfied desire.

'Ah,' she whispered, 'I am satisfied at last! We had a servant at home, a few months ago, who slept in our room, and used to tickle and play with us. She told us that men had a long thing as hard as iron, with which they pleased the ladies by shoving up their bellies, and that was how babies were made. Do you believe it? She was always shoving her fingers into us as you are doing to me now, and... and... and,' here she hesitated and seemed to shudder with delight, just as I spent all over her hand, and I could also feel her spendings come in a warm gush over my fingers. It was delicious. Her hand first held tight the top of my throbbing prick, then gently worked up and down the shaft, lubricated by my

spendings. It was indeed a voluptuous treat; I begged her to thrust her tongue into my mouth, and we continued the mutual frigging till she almost fainted away in her ecstasy.

Slightly recovering, I asked her what it was she was going to tell me about the maidservant, when she hesitated.

'Do, dearest, tell me everything,' I implored, in a loving whisper. 'We are now without reserve with each other; you can have no secrets from your loving Walter.'

'It was so funny, I don't know how she could do it, but Mary was fond of sucking and kissing us where you have your hand, dearest,' she replied, 'and it was so nice you can't imagine how we enjoyed having her do it to us.'

'My love, my Emily, let me kiss you now, and it would be

sublime if you would kiss me. I long to feel the love bites of your beautiful teeth on my Cupid's dart. Frank and Louisa are too busy to notice what we do,' I whispered in her ear, as I inclined the willing girl backwards on the soft pillow of sand and reversed my position so that we lay at full length, side by side, both of us eager as possible for the game. My head was buried between her loving thighs, with which she pressed me most amorously as my tongue was inserted in her loving slit; this was a fine gamahuche. I stirred up all the lasciviousness of her ardent temperament till she screamed with delight, and caused Frank and Louisa to enquire what we were doing, but we made no reply. She sucked my delighted prick, handling and kissing my balls, till I spent in her mouth, as her teeth were lovingly biting the head of my penis. She sucked it all down, whilst I repaid her loving attentions to the best of my ability with my own active tongue.

As soon as it was over, I took Emily by the hand, and we groped towards our companions, who, I found, were equally as busy as we had been. Frank thoroughly understood my intention; we all got together, and joined in a grope of cocks and cunnies without the least restraint, till suddenly the curtain was pulled down, and we heard the laughing voices of Rosa and Annie, as they exclaimed, 'See, here they are. What are these rude boys doing to you young ladies?'

Emily and Louisa were covered with confusion, but the girls lovingly assured them they would keep the secret, and introduce them to more fun after they had retired to bed, as it was now getting late, and we must all return to the house.

As I have before observed, the wing of the mansion in which we all slept was quite apart from the other wing in which Papa, Mama and the servants were located, so as soon as we had retired, Frank and myself joined the girls in their room, or rather rooms, for they occupied two. The Misses Bruce blushed crimson at seeing us only in our shirts, especially as one was seated on the *pot de chambre*, whilst the other was exhibiting her charms to my inquisitive cousins before a cheval glass.

'All right,' exclaimed Annie, 'my dears, everything is free between us and the boys, but we mean to punish you for allowing the impudent fellows to presume upon such liberties with you in the cave. Your bottoms shall smart, young ladies, I can assure you,' as she produced a couple of light birch rods from a drawer. In fact, I had provided them for her, the idea having been suggested to me by reading a book called *The Romance of Lust*.

A fine, large bed stood by the wall, facing another at the end of the room, but our programme only required one couch. Annie and Rosa were determined to have their enjoyment now and everyone was ordered to strip off shirt or chemise, then I horsed Emily on my back whilst Frank did the same with her sister.

Sophie and Polly were entrusted with the rods, and gaily switched us and our riders' bottoms as we trotted round the room, the sisters hardly knowing whether to laugh or cry, when a more stinging cut than usual made them cry for mercy. Our pricks were as rampant as possible, and we were not in need of any extra stimulation. Still, the girls were very hard on our rumps, although not quite so severe with the sisters. The darling Emily had so twined her legs round me as I held them close under my armpits that her pretty feet in their bewitching little slippers were frigging my cock between them most deliciously.

The sight of our red, smarting bottoms and bursting pricks was too much for Annie and Rosa, who were inflamed by lust, so throwing themselves backward on the bed, with their legs wide open and feet resting on the floor, the two dear girls presented their quims to our charge, as with both hands they held open the lips of their delicious cunts, inviting our eager cocks to come on. We charged them at once, under the impulsive urging of the rods and gave a few delightful fucking motions, then withdrew and trotted round the room again. This we constantly repeated to prolong our enjoyment, till at last the dear girls could stand it no longer, and their arms clasped us firmly, whilst the rods cut away with extra force to make us complete their pleasure; it was a most luxurious finish, and we all spent with screams of delight, and lay for a few moments in a delicious state of lethargic exhaustion till we awoke to find Sophie, Polly, Emily and Louisa all rolling on the floor in the delights of gamahuching.

After this the two dear girls begged, with tears in their eyes, that Frank and Walter would make women of them, so that they might really taste the wildest delights of love.

'Then, dears,' said Rosa, with a sly laugh, 'you must kiss them, and make their exhausted cocks stiff again, and then we will lend the two boys to you.'

We sat on the bed by the side of our fucking partners, whom we kissed, fondled and frigged, whilst Emily and Louisa, kneeling

between our knees, sucked our pricks up to standing point, as their hands drew back our foreskins and played with our balls.

Stiff and rampant as we were we entreated them to go on for a little longer, till we felt ourselves almost at spending point. Polly and Sophie arranged two bolsters and some pillows on the floor in the most advantageous manner. The sisters were each placed with two pillows under their bottoms, whilst their heads rested on the bolsters. Annie and Rosa then conducted us to the victims, who impatiently awaited their immolation to the god of love with open legs and longing cunts. The two mistresses of the ceremonies took our pricks in hand, and directed them to the path of bliss. Emily was my partner again; she threw her legs over my back and heaved up to meet the fatal thrust which was to be the death of her troublesome virginity. I had no time to see how the others progressed, but heard a smothered shriek of agony from Louisa, as no doubt Frank achieved her fate for her. My partner was more courageous, and glued her lips to mine, sucking in my tongue in the most ardent manner imaginable, even while my prick was tearing through her hymen. My spending deluged her wounded quim, and we soon lost all thoughts of pain when we recommenced a lovely fuck, with me moving slowly at first, till her rapid motions spurred me on to faster plunges, her deliciously tight cunt holding me like a hand, in fact so tight that I could feel my foreskin drawn backwards and forwards at every shove.

'Ah! you dear fellow, push on, kill me with delight!' she screamed in ecstasy, as we came again together, and I was equally profuse in my words of endearment.

As we lay still after it was over her tight-fitting cunt seemed to hold and continually squeeze my delighted prick so that by its contractions and throbbings I was ready again directly, and we ran another thrilling course before she would let me try to withdraw.

Frank and Louisa had been equally delighted with each other, and thus the two sisters lost their maidenheads almost at the same moment.

Not a day passed but we had some voluptuous games, whilst as to Rosa and Frank, they were openly engaged to be married, which was an especial gratification to the old people.

Time flew so rapidly that my visit drew to its close and we were all thinking of devising some signal display of love, to be enacted as a parting scene ere I took my departure from my uncle's hospitable and happy domicile, when one fine morning in June, who should favour us with a call, but my lovely brunette Mrs Leslie. She had driven over to invite myself and my cousins to spend an entire day before the colonel's return. 'You know,' she said, turning to my uncle, 'how stiff and starch all his ideas are, and I must have one day of real fun before he comes home from Paris. Will you let them come tomorrow and stop till the next day?'

My uncle being too kind to refuse, the arrangement was made at once. Mrs Leslie stayed to luncheon, and we took an afternoon stroll in the park afterwards. From time to time her intelligent glances assured me she was anxious for a *tête-à-tête* with me, so I asked her to take my arm and we soon managed to give the others the slip, and lost ourselves in a dense copse. Sitting down on the soft mossy turf, under a shady little yew tree, we were quite hidden from observation.

'How I longed to kiss your sweet lips once more,' I exclaimed, clasping her in my eager embrace, and sucking her breath almost away in a luscious osculation.

'If that is all you thought of, sir, you have been vastly unfaithful to your protestations of love, and I should really feel awfully jealous of your pretty cousins and Miss Redquim did I not see the unruly state of the jewel in your trousers,' she laughingly replied, as she took speedy steps to release and secure the impatient prisoner in her grasp, continuing, 'I wonder how he has amused himself since that memorable day when I first had the pleasure of both seeing and feeling the noble fellow. Now tell me true, Sir Walter, have you seduced your cousins and their friend?'

I at once made a full confession of all our amours, and begged she would indulge us in every possible way on the morrow, as it would be the last grand chance I should have before returning to town.

'A most delightful state of things, I am sure, but what a shame not to have run over and invited me to join in your amorous festivities. Surely you knew it was just what I should have delighted in. I have a great mind to disappoint you now, only I should also be punishing myself, so come on, you naughty young fellow, and I will consider between today and tomorrow what your penance will be,' she said, reclining herself backwards, her fine, dark eyes full of a humid languishing fire, which too truly indicated her voluptuous requirements.

Lifting her skirts quickly, I paid my devotions at the shrine of love by a kiss and playful bite of her clitoris, then, unable to dally any longer, placed myself between her readily yielding thighs, and was soon revelling within the soft, juicy folds of her divine organ of bliss, delighted beyond expression by the throbbing compressions to which it treated me as I lay quietly enjoying the sense of complete possession which is so delicious to contemplate, before commencing more vigorous action. Our lips met again and our billing and cooing would have lasted some time had we not heard Frank declaring to Rosa and his sisters what a damned shame it was that Walter and Mrs Leslie had given them the slip, but he would find us and spoil our fun.

This caused my charming inamorata to heave up her buttocks as a challenge to me not to waste more time, so I put spurs to my steed, and none too soon, for just as we died away in a mutual spend, Frank, sisters and co. burst upon the scene with a triumphant exclamation of 'Here's Walter and his grass widow.' Before we could recover ourselves, the laughing party inflicted an awful slapping on our bottoms, till a truce was made and we all agreed to wait patiently for the morrow's party at Mrs Leslie's.

Next day, favoured by splendid weather, we were early at the colonel's residence, and the handsome, swarthy Vishnu ushered us into the luxurious boudoir of his voluptuous mistress. 'You have arrived early, for it is scarcely one o'clock, and my toilette's not yet made, but how very welcome you all are to my house. I need not trouble to say, after the frank understanding we came to yesterday, as to our amusements now you are here. The chocolate is just ready, and I have infused in it an imperceptible something (a secret, my dear, which the colonel brought from India), which will soon set all your young, amorous blood in such a glow of desire that you will not know how to satisfy your intense cravings for the delight of love, and then naughty Walter shall be served out for his unfaithfulness to me.'

This speech made us all smile as we took up the small cups of delicious chocolate which Vishnu handed round and, as he disappeared, our hostess, who had nothing on but her dressing-gown, having drawn Frank to her side on the sofa, asked us, as the day was so warm, to throw aside as much as possible of our superfluous clothing, which was speedily done.

'We must have a romp before luncheon, then repose or stroll about during the afternoon, and in the evening we shall, I hope, enjoy some novel ideas I have quite set my mind upon,' she continued during the short time we took to disrobe. 'That's right, only keep on the *chemiserie* now, at night we will discard the last rag. I have no chemise to take off, so will keep on this convenient *robe de chambre*, but you may look, Frank, if you don't think Rosa will be jealous,' as she opened the front, and displayed to his ardent gaze all the beauties of her person.

'Even if it makes her jealous, I can't help admiring such charms!' said Frank. 'But Rosa is far too sensible for that, and thoroughly enters into all our fun; in fact, I am sure she loves Walter as well as she does me, only she can't marry both of us.'

'Ha! ha! That accounts for Walter forgetting me; so to be revenged on them both you must have me now,' she replied, lifting up his shirt to see if he was ready. 'Why your love-dart is almost exactly the size of his,' and without more ado she was on his lap, and spitted herself on Frank's cock, throwing off entirely the *robe de chambre* that she might enjoy him without impediment.

This instantly excited the girls, who lay down in pairs for a mutual gamahuche and bottom-frig, Rosa playfully telling me to let Mrs Leslie have the double pleasure by fucking her bottom as she was riding Frank.

'Hold her tight, my boy,' I said, 'and I will let her beautiful little fundament know what it is to keep a stiff prick waiting for his turn,' as I took a little cold cream from the dressing-table. Putting some on the head of my prick, as well as on the delightful, brown, wrinkled hole exposed to my attack, began to slip it in at once, despite her struggles and screams that we should 'injure her' between us. Further and further I gradually worked in, till I could feel my cock rubbing against Frank's with only the thin divisional membrane between them, our joint spendings deluging both cunt and bum, spurting the warm, frothy sperm over our balls at every thrust. This was not enough to satisfy her, and she kept us at our work until we repeated our emissions with screams of delight, and rolled on the floor in a confused heap amongst the dear girls, who were so excited by the sight of our ecstasies that they were revelling in every species of tribadism to allay their lustful yearnings.

After this, Mrs Leslie opened a side door and conducted us into her bathroom, where we refreshed ourselves and indulged in a variety of kissing, frigging, &c., but by her advice the girls refrained from exhausting us too much, and accepted cigarettes of Turkish tobacco to join us in a smoke, as we lighted some of the colonel's fine cigars. It was a picture worthy of any Apelles, as we could see the reflection of all our naked charms on the bathroom walls, which constituted one vast mirror of the very finest, silvered glass. Two rather good-looking fellows with big pricks, as rampant as could be wished, and five lovely ladies were all smoking and puffing pretty curls or rings of vapoury nicotine, alternating that sober enjoyment with the more active fun of trying to burn the tips of their cunts with the fiery end of cigarette or cigar.

About half-past two, we dressed and then took luncheon, then strolled in the grounds or on the bank of a small stream, where some of us passed the time trying our piscatorial luck, till the bell rang for dinner, which passed pleasantly enough, and at about 9 p.m., we assembled in the drawing-room, for a grand erotic *séance*.

Mrs Leslie dismissed all her servants for the night, except Vishnu, whom she said would be quite sufficient to attend to our little requirements.

The room was large and lofty, the windows closed and artistically draped with gorgeous black and gold curtains, the spaces between filled up with mirrors and branching candelabra, the opposite side of the apartment being also quite a tableau of flowers, mirrors and lighted wax candles, which shed a brilliant and yet soft, luxurious effulgence over the whole scene. Two doors at one end gave access to retiring rooms, where we undressed, and in a very few minutes the whole party, in a state of ravishing nudity, was grouped round Mrs Leslie, as she sat on an ottoman, awaiting her decision as to the programme.

She first persuaded us to sip a little of her chocolate, then went on to say, 'As we are five to two you will find I have a stock of fine, soft, firmly made dildoes to make up the deficiency in males, which, alternated with the real article, will enable us thoroughly to enjoy ourselves. First, I believe Miss is a virgin, notwithstanding all she knows and has seen; her delicate little pussy must be itching to be emancipated from the thraldom of virginity. Walter must do the service for her at once, on Rosa's lap; so now to business, as I see our gentlemen are in a beautiful state of readiness.'

Polly blushed deeply, but readily seated herself on her friend's lap with her legs wide open, presenting herself to my staff of life, whilst Rosa, passing her hands round the dear girl's waist, held open the lips of her cunny, and guided the head of my cock in the proper direction. Much as she had been frigged and gamahuched, it was a hard task; her cunt was so deliciously small and tight that in spite of her favourable position, I could only just get the head of my cock within her before she started with the intense pain, and gave a suppressed scream of anguish, the tears starting to her eyes and trickling over her blushing face.

'Courage, darling, it will soon be over,' I whispered, kissing her excitedly, whilst Mrs Leslie encouraged me by saying, 'Sharp and quick, Walter, a good thrust will force better than those gentle pushes; gentleness is not real kindness when taking a maidenhead';. At the same moment I felt she was attacking my virgin bottom-hole behind with a well-lubricated dildo, its head being well in before I knew exactly what she was doing. This and the desire to possess Polly so stimulated me that I thrust furiously at the opposing obstacle, her heart-rending cries adding to my pleasure, and making me mad with desire. At last I was halfway in, then a fierce lunge seemed to break quite through as I, at the same time, deluged her tight passage with a copious emission.

The poor little victim had swooned, but Mrs Leslie, working her dildo behind, ordered me to let my cock throb inside Polly's tight sheath, as it would tend to bring her round, and excite her amorous sensibility to the utmost.

What delightful sensations I experienced; my prick feeling all the spasmodic contractions of her vagina, and having my bottom well dildo-fucked at the same time, I spent again under the influence of this accumulated excitement just as my partner was coming round under the influence of some cordial which had been poured down her gasping throat, whilst strong smelling-salts had been applied to her nostrils. She opened her eyes, giving a violent sneeze at the same time, which vibrated on my delighted prick and which instantly began gently to bestir itself in her tight scabbard. This roused her little by little, till throwing her arms round my neck, and returning my hot kisses with all the ardour of her nature, she cried and laughed by turns, as she begged me to make haste and complete her happiness.

By a side glance I could see Frank was in Mrs Leslie's bottom, Annie in him with a dildo, and Sophie doing the same to her sister, a perfect string of pederastic branchings from my own violated bum. It was such a scene as I had never seen before, and added additional fury to my already maddened lust. I came again and again before we finished, each spend more ecstatic than the last. The chocolate had so invigorated us, that we went through an almost interminable series of spendings, till at last nature could stand it no longer, and we rolled on the floor in a confused heap and wound up in a mutual gamahuche. Mrs Leslie secured the blood-stained quim of little Polly, which she sucked till she had enjoyed the last drop of ensanguined spunk she could extract from the wounded slit of her young friend, who writhed in delight under the soothing touches of such a lascivious tongue.

It was between eleven and twelve o'clock when, just as we were recovering from a state of lethargic oblivion and thinking of some re-invigorating refreshment, the sound of carriage wheels on the gravel drive up to the house, and then a rat-a-tat-tat on the loud knocker made us all start to our feet and rush for our clothes.

'The colonel, by all that's unfortunate!' exclaimed Mrs Leslie. 'Make haste or he will catch us; who would have thought of his arriving at this time of night.'

The prudent Vishnu, pretending to be awaking out of his first sleep, so bungled and delayed opening the front door, that we were tolerably presentable by the time the colonel made his appearance, and whatever his suspicions may have been, he went through the formality of introduction in the most friendly way possible, the presence of so many young ladies evidently quite disconcerting him for the moment.

I afterwards learnt from his wife that under promise of secrecy she had confessed all to him, and vastly amused her husband by the account of our doings; but, at any rate, it stopped our fun at the time, and next day I was obliged to return to town, and thus bring to conclusion my sport amongst the she-noodles. They were anything but 'noodles' after I had so enlightened them; they were

in fact quite as knowing as Adam and Eve after they found out they were 'naked', having tasted of the Tree of Knowledge – which, in my humble opinion, meant having discovered *l'arte de faisant l'amour.*

I had to hold tight round her neck to prevent being thrown out, whilst Sophie, below, gamahuched her delighted sister, and with her right hand continued to press my balls and prick, keeping time to every insertion in her sister's bottom.

Sub-Umbra

The wind and the sun were
disputing which was the stronger...

The Wind
and the Sun

THE WIND and THE SUN

An Aesop Fable for Adults

The Wind and the Sun were disputing which was the stronger. Suddenly they saw a traveller coming down the road and the Sun said...

'I see a way to decide our dispute. Whichever of us can disrobe the traveller shall be regarded as the stronger... ..you begin..'

So the Wind blew..

...and shone.

And the moral?

Kindness effects
more
than severity.

Make love now, by night and by day, in winter and in summer.... You are in the world for that and the rest of life is nothing but vanity, illusion, waste. There is only one science, love, only one riches, love, only one policy, love. To make love is all the law, and the prophets.

Anatole France

No Tongues Stephen Bayley

Many husbands are familiar with that grudging, but nonetheless welcome acceptance of a badly timed amorous advance, 'OK, but be quick, don't sweat and no kissing.'

It is not the speed, nor the sweat, but the kissing that is interesting here. Whereas penetrative sex may be what men are said to think about 26 times a minute, sometimes more, it is significant that their partners tend (eventually) to attribute less significance to the predictable motions of the pistons and cylinders in sexual mechanics than to the more subtle and delicate operations of the lips and the mouth. One gathers that prostitutes charge more for kissing than for how's-your-father because they believe it is more intimate. A peck on the lips, then, isn't business, it's *personal*.

The kiss is unique, or at least unusual, in the repertoire of Eros, because it is both affectionate and sexual. There is no ambiguity about copulation. It is a blatant expression: lust made slippery and tangible and convulsive. Sex of the sort that operates between the hips and the knees is in and out, up and down. Sex is black or white. Kissing, however, is on a grey scale of infinite variety. We kiss children and grannies one way, friends another, and lovers in a different style altogether.

Oral intercourse is common to most birds and quadrupeds, evidence of the significance of the mouth in non-verbal communication. Deep in the thick soup of DNA, kissing may share an original significance with biting;

some male animals use their teeth the more firmly to grasp their partners while mating. I haven't tried this myself, although this prehistoric notion may contribute some of its primal force to that suspicion, hardening occasionally into a conviction, amongst many men that women to whom they are not married are inclined to bite and scream. Whereas women to whom they are married are more inclined, while on the job, to sigh and look longingly at their watches.

Despite the near-universal nature of kissing in animal behaviour, its significance in civilisation seems to be more culturally specific. The ancient Greek poets scarcely mention it, and whereas Attic vases show every variation of genital use you can imagine and some perhaps you cannot, I have never seen one showing a couple kissing.

Equally, the Celtic languages have no word for the kiss, although they may well have had many different words for bardic versions of the foregoing. But it is the far Orientals who are most ill-disposed to tongue-wrestling. Reporting from *fin-de-siècle* Japan, the travelling exotic, Lafcadio Hearn, said, 'Kisses and embraces are simply unknown... as tokens of affection.' In fact, mothers threatened their misbehaving children with a consuming and sloppy white man's kiss.

But in the nearer East, the *Kama Sutra* and *The Perfumed Garden* accept kissing as one of erotic love's more sophisticated expressive forms. The European Middle Ages saw the development of what we might call the modern kiss, although significantly it is considered a lofty refinement in the act of love, more likely practised by aristocrats than peasants. A medieval ballad called the *Glasgerion* tells the minatory story of a high-born woman who eventually realises she was bedded by a churl rather than a nobleman because while he efficiently 'got her with child' (as churls do), he never bothered to kiss her.

In contemporary Europe, the kiss has become a universal norm, except in Lapland where they seem to prefer noses. (This may be something to do with ambient temperatures around the Arctic Circle, which tend to discourage the frivolous exposure of mucus membrane.)

Cesare Lombroso states that the exhilaration of the erotic kiss derives from the oral associations of nipples and motherhood, thus transcending in its meaningful complexity even the rich, dark puzzle of sex itself. Our own slight reluctance to discuss kissing suggests a reticence that is based on something very primitive indeed. Syncopated, mutually penetrative oral sex may not replace the more fundamental sort, but it can be a powerfully stimulating prelude to the most effective forms of lubricious exchange whose rhythms, encounters and intimacies it so accurately apes.

Space does not allow even a brief catalogue of the possible variations, although the powerful, flexible and articulate tongue, with its roll, pitch and yaw facilities, is better equipped to explore than the brute penis. Quite literally, a deep, committed kiss (the French call what we call a French kiss, 'Un baiser très appuyé', or well-applied) short-circuits those carefully mapped neural pathways which link the contours of sex to the heights of taste and, by association, to smell.

The social phenomenon of air-kissing – the mwah-mwah rituals of restaurant and party encounters – may be derived from ancient olfactory sniffing, the sort dogs do around bitches' bottoms. Swahili folk have an amusing variation on this. It is, one gathers, customary for pubescent boys to raise their garments and expose themselves to society ladies who will then smell the offered member in a charming ritual called 'giving tobacco'.

Smoking is, of course, the one thing that corrupts the pleasure of kissing; Swahili or no, few enjoy the sensation of deep-throating an ashtray. If you really want to pass biological matter from mouth to mouth, I'd recommend a nice old-fashioned burgundy. Meanwhile, be aware next time you visit a Japanese restaurant that you won't find tongue *sushi* on the menu.

This article first appeared in The Erotic Review

Yes, I admit I am a libertine and in that area I have imagined everything that can be imagined. But I have absolutely not acted out everything that I imagined nor do I intend to. I am a libertine, but I am not a criminal or a murderer.

Marquis de Sade 1781

Lost
Diaries

Lost Diaries James Maclean

Mislaid Pages from the Journal of Donatien-Alphonse, Marquis de Sade

In 1764, the 24-year-old Marquis de Sade, recently discharged from the army as a cavalry captain and married for little more than a year to Reneé Pélagic de Montreuil, leaves his young wife at the Normandy property of her parents for his ornamental cottage in the fashionable Parisian suburb of Arcueil. Banned for bad behaviour from most of the brothels of Paris and under surveillance by the police inspector Louis Marais, he leads the furtive existence of a clandestine libertine.

Arcueil, October 5th, 1764

Aah… the relief of escaping from Echauffour! Even the name is claustrophobic. One more dinner party in the company of Madame de Montreuil would have induced insanity. Charming in small doses, maybe; witty on occasion, perhaps – and not at all bad-looking, it's true – but *au fond* – tough as old boots. She never draws breath and I suspect that behind that fragrant façade lurks the mother-in-law from hell. As I kissed my dear wife goodbye, her mother dropped a small bombshell: an old English friend of hers, the Countess of Stourpaine, might he coming to Paris and would I mind putting her up at Arcueil for a night or two? I had to agree without demur.

No time to lose. I want everything to be ready for my *grande partie de libertinage* next week. Wrote a note to Madame Brissault imploring her to send ten of her best girls for the evening despite what the wretched Marais has been telling her. And of course, ordered a good selection of whips, flails, martinets and canes from Jobet in the rue Tire-Bourdain. Summoned Madame Charbonfaxe to see if she could come up with some sensible suggestions about the décor of my 'special' room. I told the old embellisher that I needed something to suggest a whiff of brimstone at the same time as evoking the Grand Inquisitor's private torture chamber. 'Ah,' she twittered, 'Monsieur would certainly be interested in our Basic Black damask range. I used it to great effect when I did up the Prince de Condé's *petite maison* down the road - he simply adores it!' Not entirely sure I wanted to turn de Condé into some sort of fashion leader, but told the old baggage to go ahead anyway.

Asked my man, La Grange, to take a carriage into town and find me four girls (at least) from the stage door of the *Comédi italienne* for tonight's fun. Now that the majority of Paris' brothels are closed to me, I have to rely on his fairly reasonable skills of procurement. But I like his choice – it's so refreshingly vulgar.

Arcueil, October 6th, 1764

Last night's little entertainment – a trial run for the main event – was a success. All four girls soundly flogged. Sodomized two and took the others in the more usual manner but drank too much cognac. Got up at four o'clock to discover that Mme. Charbonfaxe had sent in her decorators while I slept and, I have to admit, the room looks so sublimely grim that I became quite emotional and my eyes filled with tears. Found one of the *Comédi italienne* actresses asleep under the table and asked her if she would enjoy, for a further consideration, christening my new 'chamber' with a sound whipping. 'All right, give me the whip and take down your breeches,' she said. Silly girl.

Arcueil, October 7th, 1764

To my rage, Lady Stourpaine has arrived quite unexpectedly during one of our nightly rehearsals — just as I was about to deflower a young seamstress. As I showed my unwelcome guest her to her room, a pair of naked nymphs flitted through the front hall hotly pursued by two priapic satyrs. To give her her due, this doughty matron did no more than snort loudly and raise one rather quizzical eyebrow. English sang-froid, no doubt. 'We shall talk in the morning, Sir,' she said, then added in an unpleasantly ominous tone of voice, 'I always rise by seven and I shall doubtless see you then for *petit déjeuner*.' And hell will freeze over, Lady S., I thought to myself.

Arcueil, October 8th, 1764

Perhaps the most unpleasant way I have ever been awoken is by the icy, foetid contents of a bidet breaking over my head at eight o'clock in the morning. Once I had recovered something approaching my normal composure, I noticed that a figure stood at the end of my bed, against the painfully strong light of an *open* window with *drawn* curtains and seemed to be saying something to me. For a moment I fancied this *contre-jour* apparition somewhat resembled an Avenging Angel. Of course, as a committed atheist I find all angels, and for that matter, God, laughable. Therefore even though I was soaked, I laughed out loud. This was a mistake. I immediately received the remainder of the bidet's contents. As it departed through the door, I heard the apparition murmur, 'I clearly remember that we arranged to meet for breakfast at seven o'clock, Sir. It is now eight. Pray be good enough to meet me downstairs at nine when I return from my morning ride.'

Later

As I dress, a terrible smell of frying ham. La Grange informs me that it is Lady Stourpaine's breakfast. These English! Not content with winning the war and depriving me of my dearest military ambition (the chance to show off my extraordinary bravery) they want to insult our gastronomic culture, too.

Later still

It is worse than I had supposed. Lady Stourpaine not only resembles the backside of an English mare and is prone to drenching her host in cold water, but she's also extremely obtuse. After giving me a short lecture on the virtues of early rising and the dangers of keeping dubious company, she could only talk of hunting foxes (at least you can eat *sanglier* – I mean, who's ever heard of *Renard à la bordelaise*, or *Renard à l'ancienne*?). This set me off on a rather brilliant (though I say it myself) gastro-philosophical discourse. At the end of it she remarked rather cryptically that that was all very well but that if God had wanted us to sit around thinking and spouting philosophy all day he would not have provided us with horses, hounds and foxes. I fear she missed my point entirely. Thankfully she's spending the day with my mother-in-law in Paris, no doubt reporting on all the activities of last night.

Arcueil, October 10th, 1764

Recently La Stourpaine and I have been following a policy of conspicuous avoidance, not always easy in a *cottage ornée*. In two days' time I will be playing host to the most sensational libertine event of the year and yet there is every indication that she will still be here to spy on me for my mother-in-law, despite the heaviest of hints that she has outstayed her welcome. Obviously the only thing to do is to persuade her that the evening will be taken up by some amateur dramatics, that this would not be something to her liking, and that therefore she should retire early. As insurance I will get La Grange to slip a sleeping draught into her hot cocoa.

Later

The conversation went something like this:

'Madame, I will be entertaining a small group of friends on Thursday to take part in some amateur theatricals.'

'How delightful, Sir! I look forward to being most entertained.'

'I fear that you will only find them tedious, Madame.'

'*Au contraire, Monsieur*. I am not averse to theatre. My late husband and I much enjoyed Mr Garrick's performances of *Hamlet* and *King Lear* at Drury Lane.'

Arcueil, October 12th 1764

The great day has arrived! Let us hope that it will not be entirely ruined by La Stourpaine's presence. The consecrated hosts have failed to appear which has also put a slight dampener on things. No black mass is complete without them. Never mind, we shall extemporise.

Arcueil, October 13th 1764

To begin with, everything went beautifully. La Grange assured me that

Lady Stourpaine had drained her drugged chocolate at a gulp and was now snoring heavily in her bedroom. By ten o'clock I had deflowered two virgins, sodomized six girls and four boys, whipped and flogged and beaten just about everybody, performed several exquisite blasphemies and, of course, had philosophised to a rapt audience between the bouts of physical activity. My energies were beginning to flag. It was my turn for a dose of the Spanish Fly that La Grange had passed around to enliven the proceedings. Just as I was about to mix some into my cognac, I noticed that everybody had fallen asleep, albeit the men with enormous erections. It didn't take a genius (such as myself) to deduce that my valet had somehow contrived to mix the sleeping draught with my best ground Cantharides.

As I wondered what to do next, Lady Stourpaine, naked and dishevelled, ran into the room. I managed to conceal myself from this terrifying old harridan and observed her discreetly from behind a column as she fell upon La Grange's somnolent form, impaling herself on his massive member with some strange English hunting cry and started to ride him as if she were pursuing the fox. Only seconds later there was a fine commotion outside and then the sound of heavy footsteps on the stairs. From my place of concealment I saw the doors flung open by liveried servants and the immaculate figure of my mother-in-law appear. A deliciously awkward pause ensued and for the first time in her life my mother-in-law seemed at a loss for words. For the first time in *my* life I allowed discretion to be the better part of valour and quietly withdrew to another room so that the two old friends might enjoy a more private encounter.

This short story first appeared in The Erotic Review

I'm gonna wash that man right
outta my hair.

Oscar Hammerstein II

Poulton

Poulton

196

Poulton

Wilkins

Wilkins

Wilkins

Wilkins

Pillow Book

Crossword 2

Solution on page 223

ACROSS

1 Don't try and join this on American Airlines – it could be an arresting experience. (4,4,4)

4 Drew Eve and slept with his daughter. Sans serif! (4,4)

6 Bawdy Chaucerian term for female part (7)

11 American for buttocks (3)

14 Poor man, everyone seems to know except him (7)

15 1970s slang term for sexual intercourse (4)

16 Made love to his sister, Drusilla, naughty lad (8)

17 Take them out of a bed, eat them, and get someone into bed (7)

18 Prevents rubbing during sexual intercourse (5,4)

21 Top deck, girls only, on the S&M route (10)

24 The DMZ between the anus and the genitals (8)

25 Archaic term for prostitute (6)

DOWN

1 Go up and see her sometime... (3,4)

2 Porcine US slang for the penis circa 1960 (3)

3 It's a chemical message, stupid. Don't talk. (10)

5 Holy shit! A'-philia' too far, for most (11)

7 Be this and double your fun, sexually speaking (2,2)

8 A long word for buggery (10)

9 Was to Lolita what GB Shaw was to Eliza (7)

10 Well, she did Dallas, apparently (6)

12 I get a kick out of you – literally (6)

13 Some women do this too, we're told. (9)

19 The sort of knowledge saintly types eschew (6)

20 Grafenberg's elusive pleasure zone (1,4)

22 Abbreviated term for the testicles (4)

23 Thrupenny Bit (3)

Shake for me girl,
I wanna be your back door man.

Robert Plant Whole Lotta Love

Anal Sex

Anal Sex Victoria Grahame

He leads me to the table, and with a master-hand lays my head down on the edge of it, and with the other canting up my petticoat and shift, bares my naked posterior to his blind and furious guide: it forces its way between them, and I, feeling pretty sensibly that it was going by the right door and knocking desperately at the wrong one, I told him of it: 'Pooh,' says he 'my dear, any port in a storm.'

From *Memoirs of a Woman of Pleasure*,
by 'Fanny Hill' [John Cleland]

The above is possibly the most famous literary reference to an attempt at buggery. Fanny, if you don't already know, eventually guides her sailor consort home to dock in the more conventional port, her vagina. It is the nonchalance with which he greets her announcement that he is about to unintentionally sodomise her which is so interesting. As far as I (and many of those to whom I've spoken on the subject) know, the practice of anal sex is far from 'any port in a storm.' No, it arouses far more passionate responses than that, be they positive or not.

Rebecca, a girl I have been close to since school is a case in point. Her introduction to anal has been a Damascus-style conversion: she, quite literally, *saw the dark*. When contemporaries at our Roman Catholic school – which had the highest teenage pregnancy rate in the county – began to embark on their first sexual encounters, Rebecca was horrified to learn of a rumour that was circulating about her classmate and neighbour, Louise. 'She let her boyfriend *put it up her bottom*,' she whispered. I simply shrugged, not because I was a cool and sexually precocious fifth former, but because I don't think I actually knew what she was talking about. Rebecca was particularly traumatised as she had let the adolescent couple use her bedroom to 'talk' in when her parents went out for the evening. Ass-fucking came to be a topic of horrid fascination and moral disbelief for Rebecca. Years later at a raucous hen night, one of the party produced a double-pronged vibrator in the shape of a thumb and forefinger moulded in plastic. Confidently, Rebecca spouted, 'You can't get two girls onto this, the thingies are too near each other.' When the other girls pointed out that the 'thingies', or probes, were not designed for two women to mount, but to fit into the holes of one, she went pale with mortification. Standing her ground she replied, 'No, it *can't* be.' Like Queen Victoria's lesbians, for Rebecca, devotees of anal pleasure simply didn't exist. I assume that she just wasn't that way inclined and that any boyfriend's exploratory fingers (doubtless there had been attempts) around her rim had received short shrift. But she was still vocal about her disdain for the activity until one night when she tried Ecstasy and had her puckered anus thoroughly ploughed by an Australian barman she was seeing. A male friend, John, colludes with Rebecca's explanation that the right time, place and man can make all the difference. John insists that he's not a bullish back-door man, but that once he'd met the girl who he thought might give it a go, he immediately manoeuvred his fingers into her tighter hole to gauge his chances of getting his cock in there too. Like Rebecca, John's girlfriend was resistant in the extreme, but came almost on the instant she was impaled.

According to Rebecca, the product of Irish immigrants, being brought up in a Catholic culture produces mixed feelings about anal sex; the sin of Sodom is also a widely practised form of contraception in devout countries as barrier, chemical and surgical methods are all strictly forbidden. Italian men, donkey-schlonged Rocco Siffredi amongst them, are reputedly more focused on the penetration of the female bottom than any other sexual practice. I am hesitant to write off a whole nation as anally obsessed, lest I should make enemies, but a good friend of mine who is engaged to a Sicilian says that it is true, or at least that her fiancé 'is a bit of a bottomite'. In my experience, men of all origins are curious about the dark star, but as to whether it is novel or normal could possibly be attributed to ethnicity. A 'Roman engagement' is a slang term for anal intercourse with a female virgin. In *Lady Chatterley's Lover*, Mellors takes liberties with milady's arsehole that her husband, Sir Clifford, describes as Italianate: 'If a man likes to use his wife, as Benvenuto Cellini says, "in the Italian way", well that is a matter of taste. But I had hardly expected our game-keeper to be up to so many tricks.' While we're on the subject of differing global attitudes to anal, I'm reliably informed that it's the common Brazilian man's ultimate sexual fantasy to 'fuck a blonde up the arse'. Presumably, if there is a post-colonial reading to be had, this desire spreads beyond just South America. Actually, who doesn't want to fuck a blonde up the arse? I would if I could.

The concept that sodomy can be employed as a method of preserving maidenhood has surfaced more than once during my research. My colleague tells me that at her university many Greek girls practised only sodomy with their boyfriends in order to hold on to virginity for the marriage bed (and of course 'Greek' features heavily in slang phrases for anal, though more often than not, homosexual). Angela Carter writes in *The Sadeian Woman* of the gang-rape of Sade's *Justine*. Justine implores the participants to spare her hymen and so is subject to multiple buggery. Carter says, '...obeying the letter if not the spirit of her request, they strip her, sexually abuse her and ejaculate upon her body... Her unruptured hymen is a visible sign of her purity, even if her breasts and belly have been deluged in spunk.'

Perversely, if the practice has a reputation for being Catholic and continental, it is also condemned for its contraceptive, and therefore unnatural use. "Sodomy" was once a generic term for any sexual behaviour which involved ejaculation without the possibility of conception; anal, oral, bestiality, pederasty even.

Like oral pleasure, anal is *extra*, not necessary for reproduction, and therefore against nature. The primary objection that women have to butt-fucking is that it is 'dirty' and surely a woman's backside is simply not designed to have a rigid phallus inserted into it, never mind have it repeatedly thrust to the point of orgasm in there, so surely anal sex is too painful to be 'normal'? All three are arguments against conquering the dark star, but all, in my opinion, make anal absolutely necessary in a sexual partnership. In response to the first charge, well, yes, it's unnatural, but so is kissing if you want to take it that far. As for painful and 'dirty', the back

passage may not be designed for reproductive intercourse, but in a clean and lubricious condition, that canal can give and receive considerable pleasure. The idea that it should be written off purely because it's painful is, I think, lacking in foresight. For a woman to complain that sodomy 'will hurt too much' to try it is peculiar. *Straight* sex is, after all, initially painful. The teenage virgin suffers rupture and sometimes bleeding when she casts off her innocence. Women are, unfortunately, accustomed to discomfort; labour pains, which come about as a result of straightforward copulation, are, I imagine a godammsight more painful than a stiff prick in the arse. With some perseverance, this sweet entry can be made love to without soreness and only irritation of an exquisite kind.

That is not, however, an excuse for you gentlemen to charge at your partner's cavity with this article in one hand and a hard cock in the other. It's not for everyone, but it's something which can grow on one given time. I must admit, it's not something I myself needed any persuasion with and was remarkably lucky to have a curious, but tender lover for my first time, who himself was also a virgin. He massaged my behind and loosened me with lubrication and adventurous fingers and slowly over a matter of several nights, slowly introduced his stiff prick to my cunt's narrower neighbour.

A colleague who has not had 'the pleasures of the back door', asked me what anal sex is like. Truthfully, I have to say that it is extremely physically pleasurable in my case. I think it feels exactly as the eponymous heroine of beating-and-buggery romp *Beatrice* describes it to her sister, 'Your bottom cheeks are deliciously elastic, Caroline. The first time you will experience considerable tightness, but you will yield. You will feel the veins, the knob, the inpushing — the breath will explode from your lungs. But on the second bout, my sweet, your rosehole will receive the repeated pistoning of the cock until you have drawn forth his spurting juice.'

After an evening's viewing of *Rocco Siffredi's True Anal Stories*, my lover and I discussed the attraction of 'the Italian way'. I suggested to him that the attraction for men was psychological rather than physical. Naturally he contested this, maintaining that the smaller passage was of course tighter, but admitted that, 'a man would put his dick in almost anything warm and wet.' As for my claim that it was primarily a mental satisfaction for a man to gain entry to that hole, he agreed that there is a desire, a controllable one at that, to be permitted into the forbidden place because by allowing it, the woman is submitting to him. OK, what he actually said was, 'It's nice to fuck the arse off a girl', but I imagine he was trying to summarise what Nancy Friday said in *Men in Love*: 'The anus becomes the most forbidden part of the body, thus invested with its own secret glamour.' For a man, to penetrate her there is to therefore reduce her to his level of animality and have his sexuality reinforced and enforced. (Is that why overgrown schoolboys and rugby players say things like, 'One up the bum, no harm done'? Whatever the hell that's supposed to mean.)

The act indicates something altogether different to the young debauched narrator of *Beatrice*: 'Sodomy — though males know it not — is an act of worship towards the superior sex. For to whatever bondage or apparent humiliations females are brought, they remain — as Aunt Maude has taught me now — the eternal victors of the act. Able as they are to receive a succession of pulsing and apparently dominant penises, it is the males who retire wan and spent.' Atta girl. There is, however, a slight hitch in claiming Beatrice's anal solidarity as a woman; she is a fictional character in a novel written by Gordon Grimley, who is, undoubtedly, a man.

Actually, who doesn't want to fuck a blonde up the arse? I would if I could.

Anal Sex

Some people ask the secret of our long marriage. We take time to go to a restaurant two times a week. A little candlelight, dinner, soft music and dancing. She goes Tuesdays, I go Fridays.

Henry Youngman

The *Restaurant*

The Restaurant
Justine Dubois

Weeping words fuel his passion. A hand touches him lightly. His tongue murmurs assent. He awakes from his dream to find her cupped close to him. Her skin is warm and perfumed. His body rises and falls in gentle inquiry, as yet unsure. Is she beautiful? He does remember her name. She does not yet, turning his arms to look at him. With soft whimperings her body spells gentle accord. Is she gentle? He cannot remember the night. Her arpeggio scent melds with their own secret perfume. It is like a shared breath between them. Her shoulder is lean and finely drawn. A blush of warmth settles on her skin. He only remembers rejection. His body begins to respond. His arms draw her closer to him. His mouth softly sweeps away the dark blonde tresses trapped beneath her necklace. The rasp of his unshaven chin grazes the pale flesh of her upper back. His hand and wrist are like fine architecture. He reaches to caress her soft round breasts, delicately assessing their weight, arousing their nipples, as strident as heaven. He cannot remember. His left hand rests briefly on her upper thigh, his fingers interlocking with hers. He strokes and separates her round buttocks, readjusting them to his lap. The girl arches her back in acquiescence. With every new nuance of movement her secret perfume injects the air, creating a bower between them. He touches his penis in reassurance, teasing at his own flesh with knowing caresses. He makes of his hand a brush of pleasure. He can feel her moistness, upturned in his lap.

Only as he enters her, does he start to remember a little. There is a moment of stillness, almost a sense of surprise, before he invents a rhythm. Still, she does not turn to look at him. His pace is deliberate and hard-hitting. He feels heavy within her. She stretches against him, lengthening her legs until she stands tiptoe on his instep. Now, finely balanced, it is she who has control. She dances upon him, evoking a faster pace. He groans in sweet delight. He remembers the woman from last night, her face distorted by anger. He recalls the dark mole on her neck intriguingly juxtaposed with the dancing drop of her earring. The girl in his arms murmurs her excitement. Again, he resumes charge, this time pursuing his massive energies deep within her. She calls out in delicious aching pain as he touches her womb. With one hand he grasps the side of her hips, with the other the small of her back, directing her, directing them both; the momentary silences of heaven.

He half-remembers the restaurant where he ate last night, its Japanese motif of sliding screen walls divided into squares of clouded glass, remembers his hors d'oeuvre of crab with lemon grass and thyme, remembers the glass of St Emilion thrown in his free, the ruination of his shirt and tie. But something else hovers at the very edge of his memory: a woman's face, exquisitely beautiful. The girl in his arms tires momentarily, no longer following their rhythm, rag doll.

Briefly, he ignores her, pursuing his angry thoughts and sensations to completion. But graciousness forbids. He allows her to come to rest, lapsing into his lap. Neither of them speaks, except in the murmurous language of lovers. He can feel her heart beating beneath her breasts; he can feel their weight, their roundness — it is a joy to him. The perfume they share is now like a room in which they might both forever live, profound and all consuming. He slips from her, shifting, to rest his back against hers. Tiredness deserts her. She is immediately alert, and bereft. With the dark blonde muzz of her hair still concealing her face, she crouches, turning towards him. He witnesses her narrow waist, the pretty length and roundness of her breasts as she raises herself into kneeling position beside him. Her scent excites him. Why was that woman so menacingly angry with him in the restaurant last night? Beneath her curtain of hair, he now sees the girl's mouth. He catches sight of its exquisite curves: the rounded edges of its upper lip, perfectly indented beneath the square tip of her nose, as sharply defined as good drawing; the generous *moue* of its lower lip which seems, by comparison, dissolved and imprecise, like a soft kiss left glancing on warm skin, a stain of beauty.

Mesmerised, he watches as this precise, beautiful shape descends upon him, witnesses it stretch to a distorted silent scream as she first nestles and then lifts to her soft, welcome mouth the bruised beautiful head of his penis, as sculptural and heavy as a column. He watches her engulf him up and down in a long-necked swallow, watches himself re-emerge tall and proud, to be conjured into even fiercer response by the cunning whip of his foreskin. No sense of responsibility fractures his desire. He recalls the woman in the restaurant saying that he was louche, that he had no pride, that he no longer made love to her. Her mouth, too, had been contorted into a silent scream, a scream of loud loathing. As she crouches by his thigh, the girl's necklace, a heavy gold chain, trails against the length of his penis. He whispers his pleasure and surprise. He is close, so very close. He can remember the woman's abuse more precisely now. She had been wearing red, a colour he had never seen her in before. She had aimed something at his head, something heavy, an ashtray maybe? It had struck the side of his temple. He had lost consciousness. He remembers the strobe of the ambulance, its siren. But why? He and his ex-wife had not lived together for more than a year. The girl in his lap senses his excitement. Still kneeling, she straddles him, riding towards his knees, the hourglass slenderness of her waist and hips revealed. As she half turns, he can just see the profile of her face. It is a face of bright joy, of delicate definition, a face of exquisite beauty. Never before.

He feels, as if for the first time, the fierce, close drag of her flesh upon his. His pleasure is mounting. He leans her gently back against him. With the soft tip pads of his long elegant fingers he caresses her. She calls out in rapture, her body racked by a new independent rhythm that repeats and repeats itself and then subsides, her blonde head sweet-comforting in the recesses of his neck. It feels as though they might have known each other forever. He remembers the Italian waiter from last night wringing his hands and murmuring 'Peccato, che peccato,' under his breath, as he and his ex-wife exchanged insults. He remembers someone trying to gently mop at his stained shirt and tie, and then tucking a piece of paper into his breast pocket. He recalls the frightened look on his ex-wife's face as she was escorted from the restaurant, violent with anger and abuse. Was it the waiter who had called the police? The girl raises herself from his lap and, as she does so he too kneels, encouraging her face downward into a pillow. He enters her from behind. She sweet-moans her approval. He strokes the long splendour of her back downwards, flattening her upper body like a cat as she arches herself towards him in welcome. Again, he moves within her, with complete authority now. Her skin has become his skin. His hand upon her has become pure knowledge. He races at her, almost cruelly now. She calls out. But he does not desist. This is his moment. He will not be cheated of its ecstasy. The rhythm between them is painful, fierce, almost dangerous. And then, at the point of her most exquisite anguish, he too calls out, an incoherent fluttering sound, and falls against her, juddering, in soft sweet acknowledgement of pleasure.

He folds her, without seeing, in his arms, her head against his chest. For a minute or two he sleeps, and then opens his eyes to look at her. She looks up at him, unashamed, her blue eyes wide open and truthful.

And suddenly he remembers their sweet darling of a waitress, with her bob of dark blonde hair, remembers her perfume and the clever shape of her beautiful mouth, remembers her tucking something into his breast pocket as he lay waiting for the ambulance on the restaurant floor. And he also recalls his wife's almost psychopathic fury as he casually confessed, 'I don't think I have ever seen a woman more instantaneously beautiful and desirable than our delicious delight of a waitress.' A barometer of anguish had swept through her features. 'I was about to tell you that I missed you.'

This short story first appeared in The Erotic Review

He enters her from behind. She sweet-moans her approval... The rhythm between them is painful, fierce, almost dangerous.

The Restaurant

Pillow Book

Crossword 1 Solution

Crossword 2 Solution

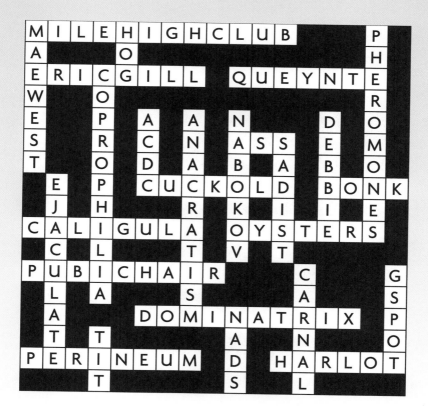

We are all in the gutter but some of
us are looking at the stars.

Oscar Wilde

Your Sexual Zodiac

Capricorn

The diligent Capricorn is a conservative soul, whose cautious realism and brilliant organising skills make them an excellent employer or worker. Their respect for authority and struggle for perfection can make them seem ambitious, cool and egotistical, but once the measure of a friend or partner is taken, the frostiest Capricorn will loosen up to give of their inner warmth.

To a Capricorn, a lover must also be a muse, a source of inspiration: private, shy and sincere, those born under this sign do not differentiate very much between sex and love. Instinctive in their choice of partner, their aim is for constancy. Ultimately, total concentration on their own and their partner's pleasure makes them superb lovers.

Aquarius

Friendly, honest, faithful, original, inventive and possessing a scientific approach. Independent and seeking freedom, yet with a sense of belonging to a universal fraternity. A tendency to be eccentric is coupled with an almost voyeuristic interest in people, but ultimately Aquarius will make a loyal friend. The Aquarian approach to sex can often be more cerebral than physical, more intellectual than sensual or passionate. It has been said that those born under this sign make better friends than lovers and that an element of modesty, even prudishness, can prevail. On a more positive note, Aquarians are rarely jealous!

Pisces

Imaginative and intuitive; sensitive, kind, compassionate and selfless, Pisces is perhaps the most altruistic of all the signs. A tendency towards self-criticism and getting too involved with the problems of others is offset by a greater endowment of talents than other star-signs. These are often used to help others or to 'swim' to the top of their chosen career. Sex is often a means of expression for the greater love that Pisceans have for the rest of humanity, especially the less fortunate. More romantic than sensual, what comes before and after the sexual act is most important for a Pisces: expressions of love and reassurance.

Aries

An Aries has all the natural energy of a born warrior. Being the most important fire sign, Aries are juvenile, primitive and enthusiastic, with all the dynamism of early Spring. They stand for beginnings, renewals and the struggle for life. They are competitive, honest, enjoy the hunt and they possess a strong handshake. Aries of both sexes adore the excitement of the chase — often more fulfilling than its successful conclusion. But once a partner has been found who is not submissive or dull or finds enjoyment in routine, then the Aries man or woman will be loyal and faithful — excitement for them is a sexual challenge or the gauntlet that their partner throws down.

Taurus

A typical Taurus is slow, strong and patient, placid and gentle – owning some of the bovine qualities we all love and admire; he or she is warm-hearted and loving, yet capable of jealousy and possessiveness. Taureans adore quality and the good things in life – they are sensualists in more areas than just sex – and can even be a little materialistic. Sex is a very natural pleasure for Taurus lovers; though potentially a little self-conscious or sensitive about their bodies, Taureans have a straightforward, healthy attitude towards making love, with no game-playing and as few complications as possible.

Gemini

A Gemini enjoys an argument and they are clever but sometimes a little cold and selfish. They can be mad-men or geniuses. Always questioning – is the alternative better for me? And the grass always seems to grow a little greener on the other side of the fence... A youthful and lively disposition helps to be very successful in the area of relationships and communicating – talking, writing, transmitting and translating. One of the most romantic signs as far as sex is concerned, Geminians find sex and relationships inextricably linked – the mind is their chief erogenous zone and they find nothing more exciting than to explore their partner's intellect too: they need more than just sex for its own sake – they want affection and friendship too.

Cancer

Cancerians are always ready to show compassion — they are kind, helpful and caring and make wonderful if over-protective parents. However, sometimes their need to safeguard can turn into possessiveness and often they will retreat within their shell, introspective and moody. The romantic Cancerian is often a shy lover, hesitant to make the first move. But once they have leapt the hurdle of their fear of rejection, they become good, un-complicated lovers, with their passions and their emotions equally divided. Occasionally they will focus on someone who cannot reciprocate their feelings and when this relationship fails they feel surprised and let down.

Leo

Leos are generous, warm-hearted, creative, enthusiastic and loving. They are courageous and honest with a sunny disposition that goes hand in hand with their handsome, often leonine, looks. This said, they can also be stubborn, selfish and just a little smug. They make good hosts and tend to accept people for what they are. Leos expect to meld friendship, love and sex in a relationship. While being unrestrained and beautiful lovers there can be something akin to an element of narcissism in their lovemaking: failure is simply not a possibility that a Leo considers in the sexual arena – if something goes wrong they become deeply embarrassed or ashamed.

Virgo

Virgos are modest, shy, practical, diligent, precise and refined. They are perfectionists and always carefully reflect before acting. They are warm and sensual and often might make perfect nurses – they are gentle, sympathetic, humane and helpful. But they can be prudish, hypochondriacal and very critical of those less hard-working than themselves. Just because typical Virgos are pure in spirit, it does not follow that they are virginal in outlook. But usually they are looking for a life-partner, not a one-night stand, and celibacy does not pose a very great problem. Virgoans prefer sex with someone who has gained their confidence and their approach to seduction will be full of charm, discernment and subtlety.

Libra

Librans strive for balance and harmony in their lives. They are diplomatic, romantic, tolerant and easy-going; also charming, sociable, idealistic and gentle. However, they can demonstrate the opposite of most of these qualities when revealing the negative side to their natures. Belonging to an extremely romantic sign, the typical Libran will place greatest emphasis on love. Though usually physically attractive and interested in sex, when it comes to the act, Librans can prove to be insecure and confused as to their sexual identity – even though they maintain a confident exterior.

Scorpio

Scorpios tend to have a remarkable presence of energy: they are determined and forceful, emotional, intuitive, exciting, magnetic, erotic, and occasionally, quite sinister. They are possibly the most passionate sign, but also the most dangerous. They never forget favours, are intensely loyal to friends and will help them unstintingly if called upon to do so. Sex is one of the most vital aspects of the typical Scorpio's life. Dominant and magnetic, the Scorpio is sexually focused and creative. He or she expects total loyalty and faithfulness from their partners and, while demanding a demonstrative love from them, tends to hide their own.

Sagittarius

The enormous charm of Sagittarians lies in their optimistic, jovial and straight-forward approach to life. An honest intellect and phil-osophical view also helps; their ability to keep their feet on the ground while aiming at a lofty spiritual or cerebral target causes them to be one of the most adaptable and open-minded of all star signs. To Sagittarians, both love and sex are free-wheeling, enjoyable adventures to be relished as much as travels over land or in the mind: those born under this sign are happy to take a risk with a relationship. The sense of touch – hugging, cuddling and stroking – is important, making them warm and sensual lovers, but for a sexual relationship to endure, they must be on the same intellectual level as their partner.

IMAGES INDEX

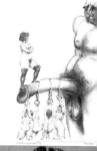